CONTENTS

At the height of the expansion of the Roman Empire, foot soldiers set fire to whole villages in Germany.

4

SPOTLIGHT ON
MEDIEVAL EUROPE

Stewart Ross

SPOTLIGHT ON HISTORY

Spotlight on the Age of Exploration and Discovery
Spotlight on the Age of Revolution
Spotlight on the Agricultural Revolution
Spotlight on the Cold War
Spotlight on the Collapse of Empires
Spotlight on Elizabethan England
Spotlight on the English Civil War
Spotlight on the First World War
Spotlight on the Industrial Revolution
Spotlight on Industry in the Twentieth Century
Spotlight on Medieval Europe
Spotlight on Post-War Europe
Spotlight on the Reformation
Spotlight on Renaissance Europe
Spotlight on the Rise of Modern China
Spotlight on the Russian Revolution
Spotlight on the Second World War
Spotlight on the Victorians

Cover illustration: A Flemish miniature from a French Book of Hours

First published in 1986 by Wayland (Publishers) Ltd
61 Western Road, Hove, East Sussex BN3 1JD, England

© Copyright 1986 Wayland (Publishers) Ltd

British Library Cataloguing in Publication Data
Ross, Stewart
Spotlight on Medieval Europe.— (Spotlight on history)
1. Europe—History—476-1492—Juvenile literature
I. Title   II. Series   940.1   D117

ISBN 0–85078–666–5

Typeset, printed and bound in Great Britain by The Bath Press, Avon

1 THE MEDIEVAL WORLD

The collapse of Rome

St Jerome, a founding father of the Christian Church, commented sadly in AD 396, 'The Roman world is falling.' Theodosius the Great, the last Emperor strong enough to hold together the massive Roman Empire, had died the previous year, and from his monastery at Bethlehem, St Jerome looked out on a troubled scene. Aleric, King of the warlike Visigoths, was plundering his way through Greece. Before Jerome's death in AD 419, Aleric had invaded Italy and sacked Rome, the very heart of the Empire that had dominated the western world for almost five hundred years.

St Jerome, the founding father of the Christian Church, teaching his followers.

From the humble beginnings of a city state in central Italy, the Romans had gradually expanded their control over all Italy, then extended their conquests overseas to North Africa, Spain and the Middle East, and north into what are now England, Switzerland, Austria, parts of Germany and France. The basis of Roman power was a magnificently efficient army of highly trained and well-armoured foot soldiers. Following the soldiers came Roman law and administration. To all corners of their Empire the Romans brought domestic peace, commercial sophistication, fine roads and grand buildings. By the fourth century AD the Roman civilization also embraced Christianity.

'I often wonder,' Adolf Hitler is supposed to have mused, 'why the Ancient World collapsed.' Minds greater than his have frequently asked the same question and come up with no satisfactory answers. Many reasons have been suggested, such as, the Romans had become soft and slothful, relying on others to fill the ranks of their armies; or the climate had changed, leading to drought and soil depletion. Some historians have even suggested that the Romans suffered from metal poisoning through the use of lead water pipes and cooking pots. Whatever the reasons, by the time of St Jerome, Roman civilization was crumbling. Grass grew through the paved roads, law and order broke down, and Europe was slipping into a long era of violent unrest.

The Dark Ages
Historians have called the period between the fifth and eighth centuries the 'Dark Ages'. The name is misleading. It gives the impression of

After the fall of Rome, peasants continued to tend their cattle as they had always done, now under new masters.

hundreds of years of violence, barbarity and illiteracy, when tribe fought tribe and the remains of Roman civilization were torn up or ignorantly discarded. The truth is much more complex.

For hundreds of thousands of peasants all over Europe, the collapse of Rome meant very little. They tilled their fields and tended their cattle as they had always done, only under new masters. Moreover, in Constantinople — now called Istanbul — Roman civilization and Eastern Christianity continued unchecked.

The Dark Ages may have marked the end of classical civilization, but they also were the time when Christianity, the biggest single historical influence on Western life, took roots. The early Church was

This detail of a painting of the fury of the Goths shows one artist's idea of what a Barbarian invasion would look like.

monastic; it was based upon hundreds of religious houses dotted over Western Europe, where monks lived and prayed, forming centres of learning, education and wisdom. After the fall of Rome, the monks of the Christian Church held Western civilization together.

We know far less about the fierce tribes which broke in upon Rome in the fifth century than about Rome itself, or about the kingdoms which were established later. In this sense the term 'Dark Ages' does have meaning: we are left with few written records of these years. As Morris Bishop wrote: 'In most of the West an architect could no longer build a dome, or a shipbuilder a war galley, or a wheelwright a chariot.' Putting together a picture of what life was really like at this time is largely inspired guesswork.

Nevertheless, amid the harshness of the centuries following the barbarian invasions, we can see the seeds of a future civilization, marked by a fresh vigour and simplicity, youthful energy, and a willingness to learn.

The dawn of the Middle Ages

The French historian Henri Pirenne claimed that the turning point between classical and medieval civilizations came not in the fifth century but in the eighth. The Visigoths crossed the Danube into the Roman Empire in 376 and swept through Greece and Italy, before settling in Spain. The Vandals set up a kingdom of destruction and robbery in North Africa, and made such an impression that their name is used to this day for those who indulge in wanton destruction. Huns moved into Germany, Franks into France, while England was overrun by Picts, Angles and Saxons. Crude though these societies were, Pirenne noted that they did attempt to copy aspects of Roman life; for example, their kings acknowledged the supremacy of the emperor, now established in Constantinople, and ancient trade patterns continued. European civilization was a mixture of the classical and the barbarian.

The event that marked the true beginning of the Middle Ages, Pirenne suggested, was the Muslim conquest of the seventh and eighth centuries. By 715 the followers of the prophet Muhammad (570–632) had established an Empire which ranged from China to the Pyrenees. In 720 they crossed into France. It looked as if the whole of Western Europe would be absorbed into the Muslim world.

'From such calamities', exaggerated the celebrated eighteenth-century historian Edward Gibbon, 'was Christendom delivered by the genius and fortune of one man.' That man was Charles Martel, King of the Franks, who defeated the Muslim armies at the Battle of Poitiers in 732. Frankish success was achieved partly by building up a class of heavily-armoured horseback soldiers, called knights. To support these expensive warriors, society developed a system we call feudalism, which became an essential feature of the Middle Ages.

The Vandals attacking Rome.

2 KINGS AND EMPERORS

The Holy Roman Empire

Charles the Great, commonly known as Charlemagne, became King of the Franks in 768. He was an intelligent man, whose kingdom covered a huge area of western Europe. On Christmas Day, 800, Pope

The coronation of Charlemagne, who was crowned Emperor of Western Europe.

Leo III crowned him Emperor in St Peter's, Rome. Three times the congregation shouted, 'Long life and victory to Charles Augustus, crowned by God, the great and pacific Emperor of the Romans.' Although Charlemagne's Empire was divided upon his death, the idea of a western empire had been reborn.

In 962, Otto I of Saxony, King of the Germans, was crowned Emperor. By the thirteenth century the emperors' official title had become Holy Roman Emperor, a form of address they were to keep until the Empire was dissolved at the time of Napoleon I.

The Holy Roman Empire was a good idea in theory, but in practice it didn't work very well. Successive emperors faced serious problems. The extent of the Empire was never very clearly defined. It usually only included those territories over which emperors could force their will. Secondly, the succession was not straightforward. The title tended to become hereditary, but officially an emperor had to be elected. Only seven people could vote and their powers were fixed by Charles IV of France, in his pronouncement of 1356, called the Golden Bull.

A further problem facing the emperors was an inability to control states outside their family territory. Successful emperors, such as Henry III (1039–1056), employed their own civil servants, called ministeriales, but these were unpopular and had few powers under a weak emperor. Finally, there was the question of relations between emperor and pope, over the appointment to positions in the Church. Frederick II (1215–1250) was the last medieval emperor strong enough to give meaning to the imperial title. By the later Middle Ages, 'Holy Roman Emperor' had become a hollow title.

Emperor Henry III employed many civil servants to control his territories.

Conquering kings

Throughout Europe, 'It was recognized in theory that the Church and the monarchy were the principal powers', according to the historian, Friedrich Heer, and kings were the most common ruling figures. Indeed, so important were medieval monarchs that a weak king brought trouble to his whole kingdom. In 1421, when the insane Charles VI was King of France, a merchant complained, 'Every day and every night one heard everywhere in Paris only pitiable outcries, because of the cost and scarcity of everything ... for night and day men and women kept crying: "Alas, I die of cold, of hunger." '

In practice, a king's throne was largely hereditary. Even when this practice was cast aside, as when Henry IV usurped the throne of

The coronation of King Henry IV of England, who seized the throne from Richard II.

King John is forced to sign Magna Carta by his rebellious barons.

England from Richard II in 1399, the successor went to considerable lengths to demonstrate the legitimacy of his claim. Henry IV proclaimed that Richard II had resigned the throne.

Medieval kings were bound by the laws and traditions of their country, and many swore at their coronations to rule within the law. A tactless or over-zealous king invariably faced revolt from his barons, the leaders of the state's most powerful families. Magna Carta, which King John of England was forced to sign by his rebellious barons in 1215, is the best-known example of subjects' grievances against a king they considered to be tyrannical. Magna Carta tried to limit the amount of money a king could demand from his subjects, and it also set out the rights and liberties of merchants and the Church. The famous clause thirty-nine states that no free man is to be found guilty without a fair trial.

Despite these limitations, however, the kings' practical powers were still immense. They selected all their advisors and decided all policies. They alone conducted relations with other states, and they could still summon their subjects to aid them with money or men in time of war. Kings had their own lawcourts and they could order subjects to attend the Royal Court to advise the king or to hear his wishes. In this practice lay the origins of the English parliament.

Feudalism
There was never a neat and tidy feudal 'system' in medieval Europe. In some countries, such as Ireland, feudalism never existed. In England for only a short while after 1066, there were comparatively clear feudal arrangements.

The feudal theory was that the king owned all the land in his kingdom, some of which, called his demesne (domain), he kept for his own use. The rest he entrusted for life to loyal companions, as fiefs. In return, the person receiving the fief, who was called a vassal, knelt before his lord in a ceremony of homage, put his hands within those of his master and swore, 'Lord, I become your man.' By this he was bound 'to love what his lord loved and loathe what he loathed, and never by word or deed do ought that should grieve him.' The king's vassal divided his land between his own vassals. Strictly speaking the feudal system did not extend to the manor and its peasants.

Feudalism was a simple two-way arrangement. The lord offered land and protection in return for service and a host of obligations. A vassal had to fight for his lord, serve in his court, and entertain his lord when he visited. A lord's permission had to be obtained, usually only with payment of a fee, for a vassal to marry or inherit his father's land. Vassals also had to pay their lords' ransom and, in one peculiar case, a vassal was bound every Christmas 'to leap before his lord, whistle and make an audible expulsion of air.'

The ceremony of feudal service. The vassal kneels before his master.

Serfs await their Lord's orders for the day.

The idea of feudalism could be seen in some of the thinking of the time. For instance, it was believed that the blood of a lord and a vassal were of different composition.

Feudalism was inflexible. It arose for protection and stability at the end of the Dark Ages but by the fourteenth century it was inadequate for the needs of society. Mercenaries replaced the feudal armies and money replaced service. Land was bought and sold, thus greatly complicating the original agreements.

3 KNIGHTS AND CHIVALRY

Knights

The military success of Charles Martel was to a considerable extent due to his use of knights, who were armed soldiers riding great war horses. The knight had now become a powerful symbol of the Middle Ages.

Knights were wealthy gentlemen who could afford expensive horses and equipment. Their life's purpose was fighting. Bertrand de Born expressed this lust for war most forcibly: 'I tell you that I have no such joy in eating, drinking or sleeping as when I hear the cry from both sides: "Up and at 'em", or as when I hear riderless horses whinny under trees, and groans of "Help me! Help me!", and when I see both great and small fall in the ditches and on the grass, and see the dead transfixed by spear-shafts!'

On the field of battle, a knighthood is bestowed by a hard blow on the neck with the flat of a sword.

The knight was a powerful symbol of the Middle Ages.

By the later Middle Ages, the ceremony for admitting a man to knighthood had become very elaborate. The ritual started with a bath, after which the candidate dressed in white and prayed in silence all night. Then followed a religious service, with prayers recited over his equipment, the attachment of his spurs, and a hard blow on his neck with the flat of a sword—the only blow he was never to return. After vows and mock fights, the ceremony was complete. The knight then joined the elite band of medieval warriors.

The knight's prime weapon was his carefully balanced and very strong sword, many of the best of which were made in Toledo in Spain. On horseback he used a ten-foot lance for attack, but then threw it away in favour of the sword, battle axe or mace. A mace was a spiked club which could smash a person's head, even beneath an armoured helmet.

In the early Middle Ages armour was chain mail, worn over a thick coat. Later elaborate plate armour was made, covering almost all of the body. Knights remained vulnerable around their bottoms, which were left unarmoured so that they could ride their horses! A full suit of armour, shield and weapons weighed over 45 kilograms (100 lbs). It is no wonder that French knights who were dismounted at the Battle of Agincourt (1415) suffocated in deep mud. Knights were so

An illustration of the knight described in Chaucer's Canterbury Tales.

King Arthur and his knights dining at the Round Table.

completely hidden beneath their armour that they devised an elaborate system of markings, called heraldry, to identify themselves.

Chivalry

In French a knight was a 'chevalier', meaning a man who owned a horse (cheval). From this derives chivalry, meaning the code of conduct a knight was supposed to follow. Knighthood was not just a job, it was a way of life which aspired to the very highest ideals of a Christian gentleman.

Chivalry, wrote a twelfth-century English scholar, meant protecting the Church, fighting against evil, helping the poor and weak, and even dying for the cause of justice and truth. The stories of King Arthur and his Knights of the Round Table first appear in the twelfth century, and incorporate many chivalric ideals and ideas. Early chivalry combined the warlike life of the knight with Christianity, and helped to guide potentially riotous soldiers along constructive paths of behaviour. By the twelfth century the ceremony of knighting had become openly religious.

As the Middle Ages drew to a close, the purpose of the knight declined. He was expensive to maintain, and common foot soldiers, armed with longbows or crossbows, or firing cannon, made the power of his ferocious charge useless. However, the aristocracy were unwilling to recognize this change. In response to the altered world, they developed and romanticized the chivalric ideal.

The courts of Europe founded new knightly orders: for example, the Order of the Garter in England, or the Order of the Golden Fleece in Burgundy, the purpose of which was,

A chivalrous knight is handed some of his elaborate armoury.

Courtly love became an important part of the chivalric tradition.

'Not at all for play or pastime,
But to the end that praise be given
First to God above all,
And also glory and high renown to good men.'

These exclusive orders, with peculiar, elaborate ceremonies for their aristocratic members, were impractical and really only excuses for nobles to be idle.

Running through later chivalry is the concept of courtly love. In past ages women had been seen as inferior to men, fit only for bearing children, and carrying out dull domestic tasks. The new view raised the status of ladies at court, making them symbols of virtue and beauty, after whom knights could yearn with romantic longings. The ideal of courtly love may strike us as rather silly, but it played an important part in elevating the status of women and introducing the romantic ideal into European literature.

The art of war
Medieval kings spent more time on war than any other aspect of government. The English King Henry II (1154–1189) was the richest man

Ten foot lances were commonly used in battles. The banners were used to identify which side each army supported.

in Europe, ruling England and the greater part of modern France. Yet, in order to preserve his inheritance, scarcely a year passed in which Henry was not fighting against neighbouring monarchs, rebellious subjects or even his own family.

Despite its frequency, medieval warfare was largely small-scale, an army comprising perhaps only a few hundred men. An army of several thousand was unusually large. Fighting was confined to the summer months, when movement along the unmetalled roads was easier.

The overriding impression of a medieval battle was one of chaos. There were no uniforms, so it was difficult to distinguish friend from foe, and without trained officers it was impossible to plan complex tactics. Peasants generally formed the infantry on either side. They were poorly armed, unwilling soldiers who merely wished to go home unharmed, perhaps with some loot or ransom.

Battle usually commenced with a charge of knights. This was terrifying, but could be halted by pits dug in the battlefield, as the Scots did at Bannockburn in 1314. A charge could also be halted by marshland, or by a careful volley of arrows. When fired from a six-foot longbow, an arrow could pierce armour at a hundred paces. The crossbow was slower to fire, but could be operated by any unskilled infantryman. Its short bolts were deadly. After a charge, the battle deteriorated

In medieval battles, poor prisoners were slaughtered to avoid the expense of their keep.

into hand-to-hand fighting, the side suffering the most casualties retiring, and thus losing the battle. If possible, knights were taken alive, for they were worth a good deal in ransom.

The carnage of a medieval battle was horrible. Poor prisoners were slaughtered to avoid the expense of their keep, and in the absence of scientific medicine, wounds turned gangrenous. The stench of war hung over a battlefield long after the fighting had ceased.

Castles

In a society geared to war the castle was essential as a fortified refuge and a symbol of status—medieval Germany had over 10,000 castles.

Early castles were just square wooden towers on top of earth mounds. Later they were surrounded by a wall, and in the tenth century the central tower, or keep, began to be built of stone. Castle design then advanced rapidly. Moats were dug, more outer curtain walls were constructed, and the keeps were rounded, to make them more difficult to undermine. Some walls were twenty or thirty feet thick. The most vulnerable part of a castle was the entrance, so here massive gatehouses were built, incorporating numerous defensive devices. First there was a drawbridge, then came one or more portcullises; huge iron grids which could be dropped over the entrance. Defenders shot at intruders

In a castle assault many different methods of attack were used.

Caernarvon castle in Wales still stands as an example of a medieval fortification.

through 'murder holes' as they zigzagged through the angled entrance passage.

Castle walls were defended by towers built at intervals along their length. From behind battlements, and through overhanging projections, soldiers shot arrows or dropped missiles or hot liquids. With its own well and plenty of food, a strong castle could withstand a siege for months.

Assault on a castle was expensive in terms of both men and money. Battering rams and catapults were built, and if the ground was suitable, mines were dug under the walls. In the end, however, unless the garrison were starved into surrender or succumbed to treachery, a direct assault had to be made by men scaling ladders put up against the walls.

Two changes made castles obsolete as fortresses. By the fifteenth century cannon were able to batter down even the stoutest walls, and the nobility were demanding more comfortable living quarters. Gradually castles were abandoned. Some were pulled down, but many remain as enduring symbols of medieval insecurity and craftsmanship.

4 THE UNIVERSAL CHURCH

Christendom

'It was not until the middle of the twelfth century' wrote Friedrich Heer, 'that the Church as an entity was even mentioned. Up to that time people thought rather in terms of Christendom.' Christianity was the great unifying force in medieval Europe. At the decline of the Roman Empire the Christian Church had divided in two. The Eastern Church centered on Constantinople, while the Western Church accepted the leadership of the pope, in Rome.

Pilgrims would cross Europe to visit Jerusalem.

The Roman Catholic Church was a truly international organization. Through its use of Latin in all services and communications, it knew no linguistic frontiers. Until the later Middle Ages, clergy moved freely between different countries, as when Nicholas Breakspear, an Englishman, was crowned Pope Adrian IV in Italy in 1154. Pilgrimages, a peculiarly medieval institution, also illustrate the international nature of the Church. Streams of pilgrims were constantly crisscrossing Europe to the celebrated shrine of St James in Compostella, or to Rome, or even to Jerusalem itself. Wherever the pilgrims travelled, they needed no passport—they were simply Christians travelling within Christendom.

The Church was almost the only patron of the arts. A monk is shown here illuminating a manuscript.

Not only was the Church a widespread organization, it was also very wealthy. Through gifts and purchase it owned almost a third of all land in many parts of Europe, and the ratio of clergy to the rest of the population was ten times that of today. Rome was at the centre of the highly complex organization of the Church. Here resided the pope, and a huge bureaucracy. In each country there was a hierarchy of archbishops and bishops to supervise the local clergy, while all Christendom was dotted with thousands of monasteries and nunneries.

For centuries the Church was almost the only patron of the arts; it controlled education at school and university; in fact, the Christian Church was medieval culture. And for the citizens of Christendom it gave meaning and purpose to life in a manner people of the late twentieth century find almost impossible to understand.

The Papacy

Pope Leo I (440–461) was the first Bishop of Rome to claim that the pope was the supreme authority in the Western Church, but not until the sixth century was the term 'papa', which was originally used for all bishops now applied specifically to the Bishop of Rome. Only in the eleventh century did the papacy achieve the power and status with which it is traditionally associated in the medieval period.

The pope's court had a curia, which was the organization through which he governed the Church. This included a writing office and financial bureau. Not only did the pope receive taxes from all over Europe,

The Archbishop reads a papal bull, a formal announcement.

Detail of a painting by Giotto of Pope Boniface, who was taken prisoner by King Philip IV of France.

30

but he also had to govern the papal states, a large area of central Italy. Among other matters, the curia issued official papal pronouncements called 'bulls', maintained the system of church courts, supervised all top-level church appointments, and decided upon canonizations. To do all this it employed hundreds of priests, lawyers and clerks. As the Middle Ages progressed the arrangement looked more like a vast industry than the centre of a spiritual institution.

Popes were elected by the cardinals, who were usually about forty in number, in a secret meeting called a conclave. As they were locked in until they had made their choice, 'the innumerable sufferings, the continual heat, the stench, the misery of confinement' made sure that the deliberations did not last too long. For much of the Middle Ages the choice fell upon wise, holy and sometimes very able men. Nevertheless, in 1305 the French King Philip IV, despairing at Pope Boniface VIII's lack of co-operation, took him prisoner and arranged for his replacement to be based at Avignon, in France. Thus the papacy began a long period of degradation. Between 1378 and 1417 there were two and sometimes three popes, all claiming to be the rightful successor to St Peter. By the later fifteenth century, in the hands of the unscrupulous and the ambitious, the papacy had reached its lowest point.

Church-State conflict
Boniface VIII was not the first pope to quarrel with secular authorities. Throughout the Middle Ages the Church came into conflict with kings and princes, sometimes with dramatic results. The problem arose because a king wishing to exercise control over his nation could not ignore the separate organization of the Church, with its wealth, law-courts and exclusive control of education. No king could govern without the bishops' aid, and therefore it was important for him to be able to appoint his supporters to the episcopacy, an institution of bishops. The popes, understandably, often thought otherwise.

The first major outbreak of conflict occurred between the Emperor Henry IV and Pope Gregory VII. In 1075 Gregory abolished lay investiture, which was the formal appointment of a bishop or an abbot by a lay ruler, rather than a member of the clergy. Henry, after meeting with his German bishops, wrote to Gregory in fierce terms: 'Thou, therefore, damned by this curse and by the judgement of all our bishops and ourself, come down and relinquish the apostolic chair which thou hast usurped.' The Pope immediately excommunicated the Emperor, and declared him deposed. The German princes took this as an excellent excuse to rebel against their emperor who was forced to back down and begged Gregory for forgiveness.

This was not the end of the story. In 1170 the English Archbishop Thomas Becket was martyred for his opposition to King Henry II of

The murder of Thomas Becket in Canterbury Cathedral.

England's proposals to limit the power of the church courts in that country. Henry's son, John, found his whole kingdom under an interdict which allowed no church services, including the burial of the dead, until he fell in with the wishes of Pope Innocent III. So the squabble rumbled on throughout the Middle Ages, although by the fifteenth century most secular rulers had found a compromise acceptable to both Rome and themselves.

Medieval witches were burned at the stake.

Parish life

Although Christianity lay at the heart of medieval society, it was not the Christianity of today. The great majority of Europeans lived in tiny isolated villages, served by priests who were frequently little better educated than the peasants who tilled the fields. The beliefs of these people were a quaint mixture of Christianity, paganism and magic, for in order that their religion be accepted, missionaries had adapted ancient festivals and customs to Christian use. Christmas, for example, was an ancient ceremony thus absorbed and given new significance.

All services were in Latin, a language which most of the congregation and many priests could scarcely understand. Churches were dark, the windows filled with stained glass, and the walls were vividly painted with Bible stories. There were no chairs or pews; the congregation stood, the weakest with their backs to the wall. In this atmosphere of mystery, stories of miracles abounded and any unusual happening was explained in religious terms. Bargains were sealed with oaths, old ladies were labelled witches and gullible men and women eagerly believed the imposters who toured the countryside selling false religious 'relics'. These relics included pieces of the 'true' cross, on which Jesus had been crucified. There were sufficient pieces of this to have built several castles. Other relics included supposedly genuine fragments of the basket used for the miracle of the loaves and fishes.

It is easy to laugh at the crudity and superstition of medieval religion. Indeed, there were many scandals, as when at the Feast of Fools priests and clerks of Paris 'danced in the choir dressed as women ... and sang dirty songs.' Yet the faith of many priests and lay people was heartfelt and genuine; the Church remained the focus of idealism in a tawdry world.

5 MONKS AND FRIARS

Monastic life

Early medieval Christianity was monastic. The tradition had been established by St Benedict of Narsia (480–547), who founded his rule at the monastery of Monte Cassino, where monks lived a life of prayer, services, study and manual labour. Benedictine monks, bound by three vows, of poverty, chastity and obedience, ensured the survival of Christianity through the troubled Dark Ages, and provided the seeds from which it could blossom again.

By the later Middle Ages there were a host of different orders to which monks could belong. Among them, from Cluny in France, were the strict Cluniacs, while in the eleventh century appeared the Carthusians, the strictest order of all. Its members were forbidden to speak,

A Benedictine Abbot (left) with a Carthusian monk.

except to God. The Cistercians, who built their monasteries in the wide open spaces away from towns, became very wealthy as farmers and sheep raisers. Ruins of their great houses in the north of England stand as beautiful monuments to a bygone age.

Life in a monastery was a continual cycle of prayer and work. The day started with the services of lauds and matins, usually at two or three o'clock in the morning. At dawn came prime, then followed terce, high mass and sexts, before nones, vespers, compline and the Great Silence finally brought the day to a close. Between these services (which had to be learned by heart) the simply-clad monks worked in the gardens or cloisters, or simply absorbed themselves in silent prayer. Once a week monks in the Benedictine order met in the chapter house to hear a reading from the Rule of St Benedict.

Good food and drink were considered to be very important in some monasteries.

Even in the strictest monasteries, of course, the monks had to pause for meals. In some of the more easy-going houses these breaks seemed to become more important than the services themselves: a scholar visiting Canterbury in 1179 complained bitterly at being served no less than sixteen dishes!

The living Church

The medieval Church was never static. One of its great strengths was its ability to revive and reform itself after a comparatively settled period. Only at the very end of the Middle Ages did the Church lose this flexibility, failing either to absorb or adapt to the criticisms of the early Protestants.

The Cistercians were a good example of the Church renewing itself. The eleventh-century monks of Cîteaux felt that St Benedict's rule was not being followed sufficiently carefully, and they swore to follow it to the letter, 'rejecting everything that was contrary to it'. Because

Geoffrey Chaucer attacked the wealth and immorality of the clergy in The Canterbury Tales.

The Dominican and Franciscan orders being confirmed by Pope Honorius III.

St Benedict's monks did not have peasants to do their work for them, they claimed, neither would they. By the thirteenth century there were about 700 Cistercian houses for men and women.

Convents were founded by spiritually inspired women, although their numbers were far fewer than male houses. The problem for convents was that they tended to be used as convenient retirement centres for wealthy spinsters. With such inmates, they soon lost their zeal and, especially if they were situated near a monastery, they easily became the target for scandal.

Following the great spiritual, artistic, intellectual and social revival, sometimes known as the 'twelfth century renaissance', criticism of the Church grew. The chief complaints were that the clergy were wealthy, idle and immoral. Nowhere are these attacks more vividly portrayed than in Geoffrey Chaucer's *Canterbury Tales*, in which the men and women of the Church (except the poor parish priest) are rebuked for their worldliness.

St Francis

While monks renounced the world, friars lived in it. There were four groups of friars: Franciscans, Dominicans, Augustinians and Carmelites. Most of them lived by strict rules, wore simple clothes called habits, and moved among the people of town and country, preaching, praying and living on charity.

37

St Francis left behind his life of riches to serve God.

As a young man, St Francis (1181–1226) lived a thoughtless life of luxury. At the age of twenty-one, however, he was imprisoned and fell ill, during which time he heard God calling him to His service. St Francis swapped his rich clothes for rags, gave away all his money and made a pilgrimage to Rome. Despite their renunciation of worldly comforts, Francis and his followers were marked by their bubbling happiness: they would enter a town singing, and laughed when scorned for their dirty appearance and unusual behaviour. Francis did not like rules and he had no intention of founding an order: he once closed a Franciscan house of study with the words, 'It is my desire and will that my brethren, following the example of Jesus Christ, shall give more time to prayer than to study.'

Despite the example of Francis's own life and his express wishes, his followers soon became carefully organized, and in time they grew wealthy as gifts were showered upon them. The image of Friar Tuck, a fat, worldly fellow, comes from the later Middle Ages and shows just how far the ideals of St Francis had been warped in the popular imagination.

Dominican friars, founded by the friend and ally of St Francis, Dominic of Calenega, were noted for their learning. Their schools at Paris and Oxford were the intellectual centres of Western Europe. St Thomas Aquinas (1225–74), one of the greatest of all medieval philosophers, was a product of a Dominican training.

6 THE LABOURING POOR

The village

The vast majority of the inhabitants of medieval Europe were poor peasants. They lived by agriculture, scraping a subsistence from broad fields or stony terraces, sharing common pasture with their colleagues. In years of good harvest they survived in comparative ease. All too frequently, however, the crops, grown without any modern fertilizers, drainage or machinery, failed. With the winter came starvation.

A modern visitor to a medieval village would be horrified at the dirt and squalor. Peasant housing throughout Europe was below a standard we would consider suitable for animals. Their stone, wood or mud huts, surrounded by small gardens, were usually a single room, without windows or fireplaces. In winter one end of the hut could be fenced off for animals. Furniture was rudimentary, lavatories

Peasants plough the land for their lord.

The surnames of many people are derived from the trade of their ancestors, such as this blacksmith.

non-existent, and water had to be drawn from a well or stream nearby. Men and women wore simple clothes of wool, linen and leather.

Each village was a self-contained unit, centred around the church, with perhaps a square or village green where meetings and entertainments were held. Each community had its blacksmith, miller, brewer, weaver, carpenter and others whose trades have passed into the language as familiar surnames. Large and expensive equipment, such as a plough, a cart, or a team of oxen were shared, no ordinary individual having the wealth to own such a precious item.

The manor

The most common unit of organization in medieval society was the manor. By the ninth century it was found in parts of Italy, France and Germany, from where it spread to much of the remainder of Europe, although never to some parts of the Netherlands or Scandinavia. The essential feature of the manorial system was that the peasantry were subordinate to the lord of the manor, who owned most of the

In many parts of Europe, each family farmed a small strip of field beside their village.

land. The lord had certain rights, such as to demand labour from peasants on his land, or to insist that they had their corn ground in his mill—for a fee. In some countries the peasants had to give their lord eggs at Easter, and there were hosts of other irritating duties, such as paying the lord a death duty when a peasant died. Payments to the lord were usually made in kind (a goose, a sack of corn, etc) until the later Middle Ages.

In return for their service and payments, the peasants were allowed to work land which belonged to the lord. In many parts of Europe the village fields were divided into two or three huge areas of up to 400 hectares (1,000 acres) of land. Each family farmed a number of small strips. Cattle and pigs fed in commonly-owned meadows, woodlands or open heaths.

Of course, not all European peasantry was bound by the strict manorial system. Moreover, as the economy became more sophisticated and particularly after the Black Death had reduced the population dramatically, peasants found their traditional burdens increasingly irksome. By the close of the Middle Ages the manorial system in Western Europe served little useful purpose.

Birth, marriage, death

Only gradually are historians discovering what daily life was like for ordinary men and women in the Middle Ages. Our interest is no longer exclusively on the royal, the noble and those with political power.

41

Babies were baptized as soon as possible in case they died.

While perhaps no less interesting than those of the great, the lives of the common people are far more difficult to understand. We have few written records, and what we know has to be pieced together from references in other works, such as parish records (where they exist), poems, songs, carvings and even stories and folk tales.

We do know that life was less highly regarded in the Middle Ages than today. It had to be, for the expectation of life scarcely exceeded thirty; a man of fifty was old. Childbirth was a constant danger for both mother and child. Many women bore a child each year of their marriage until either the process killed them, or they survived past child-bearing age. Birth control was rarely understood, and the science of midwifery equally haphazard, especially as the connection between dirt and disease was seldom made. Kings bathed occasionally, peasants never.

The age of marriage varied considerably between different parts of Europe, social classes, and economic conditions. In very poor and remote areas formal marriage might not even occur, while among the rich, child marriages were arranged for dynastic reasons.

Death was ever present. In the average-sized village there must have

In an average-sized village there must have been at least one funeral each week.

The Black Death killed between one third and a half of the population of Europe.

been a funeral each week. A child would almost certainly have lost at least one parent by the time he or she was a teenager, and the majority of babies never reached their fourth birthday. The killers were diseases virtually unknown in Western Europe today. The most devastating of all was the plague.

The Black Death

'In their bones they bore so virulent a disease that anyone who only spoke to them was seized by a mortal illness and in no manner could evade death.' So spoke a chronicler of a party of sailors arriving in Sicily in October, 1347. The dreaded illness was bubonic plague, commonly known as the Black Death because of the dark swellings it produced on the victims' bodies. Its arrival in Sicily marked the beginning of Europe's most horrifying disaster.

From Sicily the disease spread along trade routes to Italy, France and Germany, finding its way to Britain by August 1348. It is now thought that the illness was carried by fleas, common parasites on human beings. The Black Death took three forms, infecting either the lymph nodes (leading to the black lumps which gave the disease its name), the lungs and throat, or the blood. In all three cases it usually proved fatal.

44

The disease was most virulent in the rat-infested, unhealthy towns. Some were left derelict as survivors fled to the countryside, but even here there was little respite as whole villages were wiped out. Jails were emptied, crewless ships drifted on the oceans, and families abandoned each other. Cattle and other animals also died of the disease, while crops rotted in the fields for want of farmers to harvest them. To a superstitious people, it really seemed as if the end of the world was at hand. Between one third and a half of the population of Europe was wiped out. Fear overran the continent.

The economic and social effects of the Black Death were considerable. Prices rose. Since labour was scarce, people were able to demand higher wages. Serfs bought freedom and the end of the manorial system was hastened by serious peasant revolts, such as that in England in 1381. And, as if the Black Death was not horrible enough in itself, all over Europe there were outbreaks of fierce persecution of the Jews, who were illogically blamed for the plague.

Christians illogically blamed the Jews for the Black Death and hundreds were burned alive.

7 TOWNS AND TRADE

Towns

Most medieval towns were little more than large villages, with populations of little over 1,000. By the thirteenth century the population of London, by far the largest town in the British Isles, had risen to 30,000, while Milan, Venice and Paris had expanded to over 100,000 inhabitants each.

By the thirteenth century, Paris had over 100,000 inhabitants.

There were three types of town. Firstly, there were the ancient foundations, such as Canterbury or Pisa, whose origins lay in Roman times or before. In southern Europe these great cities were frequently able to free themselves from the surrounding kingdoms, forming wealthy city states, such as Florence. A second type of town was that which grew in medieval times from its village origins. There were hundreds of these all over Europe. Many, like Coventry, grew because of the construction of a cathedral in their midst. Finally there were new towns, such as Salisbury, established by kings, barons, clergymen or merchants.

Almost all towns of any size and importance gained a degree of self-government, which varied from the total independence of

Castles and towns surrounded themselves with high walls for protection against attackers.

Town dwellers and merchants bargain in the market.

Frankfurt in Germany to the limited privileges granted to English towns in their royal charters. For their own defence the townspeople surrounded themselves with high walls, within which houses and shops crowded in upon themselves as prosperity increased. They were centres of wealth and freedom, ('Town air makes men free' ran the old adage) but also of disease and danger, since they had no adequate water or sewage systems. They tended to attract vagrants and thieves from the surrounding countryside.

Trade and communications

Although European trade had been drastically cut back during the Dark Ages, it never ceased entirely. Scandinavian furs were always in demand in the South, while Venice maintained a prosperous trade with the eastern Mediterranean.

By the eleventh century, however, Europe had settled down and trade was flourishing once more. English wool and tin were carried all over Europe, while in return the northern nations imported salt, wine and luxuries from the East. By the fourteenth century European trade had reached a high degree of sophistication, and taxes on goods entering and leaving the country formed a considerable part of a king's revenues. Up and down the continent, by sea, river and road there was a continual stream of commerce in every conceivable article, from Italian marble for the construction of northern cathedrals, to coal from Newcastle for fires in Germany.

48

Sea-trading merchants wait at a port for trading ships.

Almost all roads were terrible. Merchants travelled in convoys of pack horses or mules, well armed for protection against robbers. In winter many routes became impassable. Wherever possible, heavy goods were transported by water. Rivers that ran far inland, such as the Rhine or Seine, were as invaluable as modern motorways, and most cathedrals were built near a river up which the heavy stone required for building could be transported.

The burgesses were the wealthy, well-dressed town dwellers.

Ocean-going ships developed slowly and most captains were unwilling to sail out of the sight of land. For safety they preferred to sail along the coast. Galleys remained in use in the Mediterranean because sailing vessels were unwieldy and slow. Nevertheless, by the fifteenth century, European sailing skills had developed far enough for explorers to be on the verge of tremendous discoveries.

Manufacture and mining

One of the most significant developments in European society throughout the Middle Ages was the growth of a merchant class. In the comparatively static and warlike society of the tenth century it was considered sufficient to divide workers into soldiers, priests and labourers. Three hundred years later not only had a class of town-dwelling merchants called the bourgeoisie emerged, but one contemporary felt it 'to be the best estate of all; they live in a noble manner, wearing lordly garments ... When the vassals go to be massacred in battle, the burgesses (town dwellers) go to picnic by the river.'

Some merchants made their money in trade, others by lending money (at up to 100 per cent interest!), while there were also fortunes to be made in manufacture and mining. The most widespread manufacture was that of cloth, since everyone needed clothes. Wool was the usual raw material, and England the source of the finest fleeces. Articles

50

Weaving woollen cloth on a German hand loom.

were manufactured in Flanders or Italy—by the early fourteenth century there were 300 clothing workshops in Florence alone. Other important goods manufacture were bricks, weapons, tanned leather, pottery, and soap.

Metals were mined all over Europe, although mine shafts and galleries were often extremely dangerous. Miners frequently lost their lives through flood, explosion or collapsing roofs, while searching for gold and other minerals. When no natural explanation for a disaster could be found, it was put down to the work of underground demons.

8 THE WORLD OF LEARNING

The role of the Church

For hundreds of years after the collapse of the Roman Empire all academic learning was based on the Christian Church. Practical matters, such as the art of constructing a mill or shaping an axe, were taught as they always had been, by example and experience. Only the Church, with its need to have priests and monks who could sing

Some monks studied mathematics in their quest for knowledge.

and read Latin, preserved the literate skills. A few enlightened monarchs, such as Charlemagne or Alfred the Great (871–900), supported the Church in its endeavours, but in much of their work the priests struggled alone.

From the eleventh century onwards education and learning flourished, and gradually the hold of the Church slackened. But the process was very slow. The Church held that 'man's exile is ignorance; his home is knowledge', and generally it did all it could to satisfy peoples' thirst for learning. Universities grew up under Church auspices, while the monasteries were real centres of art. They had their own choir schools, in which students were taught to chant in Latin. Basic grammar was also taught, with perhaps a smattering of philosophy and Christian theology. In the cloisters, monks painstakingly wrote out the beautiful manuscript books, which were so valuable in the days before the advent of printing.

One of the first acts of St Augustine, when he arrived in Kent at the very end of the sixth century, was to establish a school at Canterbury for the training of priests.

Schools
The children of the nobility and those of most wealthy burgesses did not go to school. They were educated at home by private tutors. Very few girls ever received formal instruction, and the few who did were taught in convents. For the peasants there was no education.

Although a few secular schools survived from Roman times in southern Europe (particularly Italy), most European schools were 'grammar' schools, which developed from cathedral schools. They followed a curriculum based upon that of the Romans: grammar, logic and rhetoric, called the trivium, and arithmetic, geometry, astronomy and music, called the quadrivium. Some schools, for example the famous school at Chartres in France, taught other subjects, such as medicine.

By the tenth century, Salerno, in Italy, had an important school of medicine free from church control. The first school with such freedom in England was Winchester, which was founded in 1382. Most other English grammar schools, such as that at Canterbury, had to wait until the reformation before they could gain similar independence.

School hours were long and the discipline was strict. While at school pupils were not allowed to speak any language but Latin. The reason for this faith in the value of classical learning was clearly put by Bernard of Chartres: 'We are like dwarfs seated on the shoulders of giants; thus we see more things than the ancients.'

Learning was usually by heart, for paper was too expensive to waste on boys, and the only other writing surface was a slate. Modern pupils find the feats of memory accomplished by their medieval counterparts

In a medieval school room, children who misbehaved were punished severely.

very daunting; it was not uncommon for them to commit thousands of lines to memory, encouraged by the teacher wielding a 'palmer' with which to slap their palms or bottoms if they forgot.

Universities

Universities are of medieval origin. In Italy they grew up around groups of students attached to particular teachers, the first being at Salerno. In Bologna the students could fine teachers who dodged answering tricky questions! In the north, universities were formed by societies or guilds of teachers. Most were not consciously founded at any particular date; they just emerged, and then were given official recognition by a royal charter, such as that given to the University of Paris in 1200.

The word 'universitas', from which 'university' originates, means little more than a corporation, and early universities had very little formal organization. There were no official university buildings: stu-

Alchemy was a subject of great interest and amusement to many medieval scholars.

The study of astronomy became quite sophisticated by the end of the medieval era.

dents lived in any convenient boarding house (these became the colleges of Oxford and Cambridge), and the students could be of any age. A graduate of fifteen was not uncommon.

The subjects offered for study were the trivium and quadrivium, with others, such as law, in addition. Teaching was by lecture, with the students taking notes on wax tablets, often starting at dawn and continuing until the early evening. An unusual feature of academic life was a form of medieval 'university challenge'. A bright student announced a bold theory before a large audience, then defended it against critics, the crowd of onlookers applauding witty or clever argument.

A more violent feature of universities was the frequent 'town versus gown' friction. At times the tension between the students and the town in which they lived became so great that fighting broke out; at Oxford in 1355 many were killed in the Great Slaughter. The teasing of new students was more good-humoured, but even this became out of hand at times, so that a German law of 1495 ran: 'Each and every one attached to this University is forbidden to offend with insult, torment, harass, drench with water or urine, throw on or defile with dust any new student.'

Medieval literature and thought

Those born into the twentieth century are accustomed to change in every aspect of life, from science to singing. In fact, change for us is the normal state of things. For men and women of the medieval period the opposite was true. Life did not alter much from generation to generation, and where there were differences they frequently came

Some historians believe that chess was introduced to Europe after the first crusade.

Medieval books were often beautifully hand-illustrated.

slowly. One pattern of life is not necessarily better or worse than the other, and we should beware of criticizing our medieval ancestors for habits of thought and literature which appear dull and unimaginative to our restless civilization.

To begin with, the vehicles for change were largely absent from medieval society. Transport was slow and difficult. Education was for the few; books were rare and hand-written—even paper was unknown in Europe before the twelfth century. Until that time science and mathematics was also limited by the use of Roman numerals. Moreover, without radios, television or newspapers, contact between cultures was suspicious and slow.

Medieval thought was a blend of Christian revelation and Greek reason, mainly based on the work of Aristotle, a famous Greek philosopher. No one combined these two opposites more skillfully than the great thirteenth-century philosopher, Thomas Aquinas, an Italian Dominican friar.

Most medieval literature has been lost over the centuries. What remains is brilliantly colourful and fresh. Two major developments marked the period: the growth of written and vernacular (as opposed to Latin) literature. For English readers nowhere are these two more obviously united with poetic genius than in the work of the writer Geoffrey Chaucer (1340–1400), whose most famous poem is the *Canterbury Tales*.

9 ARTS AND ARCHITECTURE

Cathedrals

The grandest and most enduring monuments of the Middle Ages are the cathedrals dotted all over Europe. From the magnificent domed cathedral of Florence, to the soaring simplicity of Salisbury, they remind us most forcibly of an age in which people's aspirations sought heavenly rather than worldly goals. And lest we see the cathedrals as isolated and rare creations, Europe's host of parish churches teach us otherwise.

The great wave of European church and cathedral building started in the eleventh century. The need, in a society where at least half the population attended mass on Sundays, was for large buildings. Their form was that of the cross, their construction of stone, with stout pillars and round arches. In troubled areas the church doubled as a place of refuge when danger threatened. The early style of architecture we term 'Romanesque', for it echoed the classical buildings of the fallen Roman Empire.

In the twelfth century a new Gothic style emerged. This featured pointed arches, lighter pillars and broader windows. This style reached its height in the sixteenth century in England, with delicate fan vaults and scarcely-supported windows. Other parts of Europe followed different styles. In France cathedrals developed a flamboyant riot of tracery, with sweeping buttresses and ornate carving. On the other hand, by the fourteenth century Italian architects had begun to move back to classical inspiration, heralding, with their domes and round arches, a movement later termed the Renaissance. With such developments the waning of the Middle Ages had begun.

Domestic architecture

With the exception of castles, it is difficult to speak with authority about medieval domestic architecture. The houses of the poor were usually too flimsy to last for more than a generation or so. Those of the wealthy were invariably pulled down or improved out of all recognition, to keep pace with changing fashion and requirements of comfort.

In the villages of the tribes which swept over Europe during the Dark Ages the hall was the most important building. This was simply

The soaring simplicity of Salisbury Cathedral, an enduring symbol of the Middle Ages.

Ightham Mote in Kent is a fine example of a medieval semi-fortified manor house.

a large barn where the lord and his supporters and dependants ate and slept. It was not divided into rooms. As times became more settled, however, needs changed. More substantial stone halls were constructed, with separate kitchens and a private area at the end of the hall for the lord and his family.

By the end of the Middle Ages the hall had developed into the semi-fortified manor house, in which a strong wall contained the house

61

Medieval craftsmen were skilled in the art of stone carving.

itself, together with stables and a gate house. Within the house bedrooms were built, perhaps on the first floor, and fires in grates with chimneys kept the occupants warm in winter, without smoking them like kippers. Tapestries lined the walls, and furniture became more comfortable and refined, especially in the bedroom.

Town houses of the bourgeoisie were often the most comfortable of all, being less draughty. Several storeys high, they were richly decorated with hangings and beautiful furniture. They might even have a room specifically set aside for bathing. The lavatory remained primitive: scarcely more than a hole in the floor over a barrel in the basement, which had to be emptied periodically.

Painting, sculpture, music

As with almost all the medieval arts, painting, sculpture and music were essentially religious, at least until the thirteenth century. The aim of medieval artists was to offer a representation. They cared little for perspective or accurate portraiture, but more for colour and pattern. The most beautiful examples of their work are to be found among the pages of illustrated manuscripts or in the glorious stained glass windows of churches and cathedrals.

At first sculpture was equally symbolic, but gradually realism increased, especially in the figures carved on tombs. The sense of humour of the time can be caught from the gargoyles on the outsides of buildings, and the carved misericords, against which footsore monks could lean during endless services throughout which they were expected to remain standing.

The renaissance in painting started in Italy, perhaps with Giotto (1266–1337). From here it spread to the Flemish school of artists. Its features were a new, realistic style, based upon perspective, attention to light and shade and care for accuracy.

Music developed as rapidly as other art forms during the medieval period. Because they were not written down we know little of the countless folk songs which must always have been on people's lips. The Church, especially the Franciscans, set a high store by musicality. The thirteenth-century Brother Henry of Pisa, won high praise for his 'great and sonorous voice' which 'filled the whole choir'. Formal music developed from the simple plain song chant of monks to a time at the end of the Middle Ages when every self-respecting prince had his private orchestra. We would not recognize all the instruments, but the roots of modern music had been planted.

Formal music developed from the simple chanting songs of monks, seen here singing together.

10 CONTACT WITH ISLAM

The Islamic offensives

Islam was the last of the great world religions to be established, but it spread more rapidly and fiercely than any other. As we saw in Chapter 1, between the death of the prophet Muhammad in AD 632 and the first half of the eighth century, Muslim Arabs carved out a vast empire. Only when this Empire reached the limits of communication and its forces were spread very thinly were the Christians of the West able to contain it. Relations between the two cultures then remained strained, but comparatively peaceful.

The Byzantine Empire bore the brunt of the struggle with the Arabs. By the eleventh century Christian pilgrims were free to visit Jerusalem, a city also holy to Muslims. There was extensive trade between East and West, sometimes via Constantinople. The West generally benefitted from the Arabs' advanced knowledge of science, classical scholarship, medicine and many other branches of learning.

At the end of the eleventh century, however, the era of co-existence came to an end. Fierce Seljuk Turks moved in from the East, defeating the Byzantine army, capturing Jerusalem, and persecuting Christian pilgrims. The Emperor of the East appealed to the Pope for help. Urban II called all Christians to arms to drive out the Turk. His speech to the Council of Clermont in November, 1095, was one of the most powerful ever delivered: 'If you wish to be mindful of your souls, advance boldly as knights of Christ to the defence of the Eastern Church ... Drive out the Turks who are in this land, and may you deem it a beautiful thing to die for Christ in that city in which he died for us.' The First Crusade had been launched.

The crusades

The crusades were a series of campaigns by western rulers and their armies, fought between about 1095 and 1291, to recover the Christian holy places in Palestine from the Muslims. From a military point of view they were a spectacular failure, for by the time the final army was defeated in 1291 and the city of Acre had fallen to the Muslims, the Christians retained not a metre of Palestine.

The motives for the crusades were not as straightforward as they might appear. For many they were indeed a holy war, but for thousands

Pope Urban II preached the first crusade to Jerusalem in 1095, at the Council of Clermont.

of others they represented a chance for plunder, land and easy wealth. Since successive popes promised remission of sins for crusaders, some left for the Holy Land with a light heart, glad to leave tricky situations

The Children's Crusade of 1212.

behind them. After all, the job of the knight was to fight, and what could be more apt than battle with the infidel?

The stories of the eight crusades are a bloody blend of tragedy, valour and honour. The first crusade managed to capture Jerusalem in 1099, then set about massacring the inhabitants: 'Piles of heads, hands and feet were visible in the streets, so that it was necessary to pick one's way carefully over the bodies of men and horses. But this was nothing compared with what happened at the temple of Solomon ... where men rode in blood up to their knees and bridle reins. Indeed, it was a just and splendid judgement of God that this place should be filled with the blood of unbelievers.'

Nevertheless, Jerusalem was soon recaptured by the Turks, and successive crusades had at best only limited success. One was made up of children, another sacked Constantinople before it reached the Holy Land. The crusades were not one of medieval Europe's noteworthy achievements.

Broader horizons
Shameful though the crusades might have been, their effects upon western civilization were considerable. They marked the West's rediscovery of the East. Many were the immediate and obvious benefits brought by a boom in international business. Rice, sugar, lemons, spices, rugs and satins all appeared in western markets. To the rough cultures of north-west Europe these represented untold luxury. Arabic numerals and learning were warmly received. But perhaps the greatest effect was in a change of outlook. The early medieval world had essentially looked inwards or upwards. Now men and women of learning and imagination were aware of a rich and exciting world outside the boundaries of Christendom.

One of the greatest medieval travellers was Marco Polo. Inspired by stories of eastern wealth, at the end of the thirteenth century he travelled to China and back, bringing stories of a wonderful civilization. One hundred and fifty years later, intrepid European sailors were trying to reach China and Japan by sea. Gradually the Portuguese edged their way round Africa, while ships of other nations tried to find a western route to the east, across the Atlantic. The breakthrough came in the 1490s. During that decade Vasco da Gama sailed to India and returned safely, while Christopher Columbus and his successors discovered and explored what turned out to be a new world in the west.

Before long Europe had become a westward-looking continent. The focus of power shifted from Italy and the south, to France, Britain, Spain and the Netherlands. For a people accustomed to clear answers within a heaven-established framework, overseas exploration raised more questions than it answered.

Marco Polo sets sail for the Far East from Venice.

68

11 THE END OF THE MIDDLE AGES

Renaissance

It is the job of the historian to impose some sort of order on the chaos of the past. To do this he invents labels for periods, one of the most widely accepted of which is the term 'Middle Ages'. Yet at no time did the Middle Ages suddenly end, any more than they began in a particular year. All we can say is that the European world of 1600 was vastly different from that of 1400, and that over those two centuries we pass from what we call the medieval to the modern age. The change is like that of the seasons—we know that July is summer and October autumn, but precisely where the dividing line comes, no one can say.

Certain changes heralded the end of the Middle Ages, most of which have already been noted. Individually they might not have meant much, but together they altered the world. Foremost among them were the Black Death, with its dramatic effect upon the decaying manorial system; the overseas explorations and discoveries; the arrival in the West of gunpowder, which revolutionized warfare; and printing, which enabled ideas to be spread as never before. During the fifteenth and sixteenth centuries, towns, trade and manufacture expanded rapidly, creating a new, more sophisticated economy.

The term 'Renaissance' means 're-birth', and it is taken to mean the new interest in classical arts and learning, which blossomed in the fifteenth and sixteenth centuries. Architecture, painting, music, sculpture and literature were all affected by humanist thinking, which raised the individual man from the insignificant status afforded to him in the Middle Ages. The great sculptor Michelangelo's magnificent statue of David is a perfect symbol of the new thinking.

Reformation

Long before the end of the Middle Ages it was quite clear that all was not well with the Roman Catholic Church. With the papal exile in Avignon, the papal schism and disreputable characters holding office, the papacy had sunk to a low ebb. Moreover, although the clergy had always been favourite targets for laymen's scorn, by the fifteenth century criticism seemed to gain a fresh urgency. Men and women needed spiritual comfort, which the Church seemed unable to provide.

The papal palace of Avignon still stands as a reminder of the papal exile in the Middle Ages.

The Englishman John Wycliffe had been calling for reform in the Church as early as the end of the fourteenth century. In the next century, John Huss, a Bohemian preacher, was so impressed by these calls that he led a national armed revolt against both pope and emperor, which ended in his execution.

The turning point came in 1517, when a German monk, named Martin Luther, began a battle with the Roman Church which eventually split it, and led to the bitter division of Europe between Protestant and Catholic. In Protestant countries, such as Scandinavia and Holland, papal authority was denied, and the hierarchy of bishops, cardinals, deacons and priests was abolished. Monasteries were closed, as seats of sin; churches were cleansed of ornaments and decoration that might detract from the worship of God; church teaching was altered, and the Bible was translated into the language of the common people, so they could read it and interpret it for themselves. With such changes, the Middle Ages had certainly come to a close.

GLOSSARY

Architect   A person who designs a building.

Barbarian   Roman term for a member of an uncivilized tribe.

Bourgeoisie   Wealthy town dwellers, generally conservative and materialistic.

Bulls   Official sealed papal documents or pronouncements.

Buttresses   Constructions built of brick or stone to support a wall.

Bureaucracy   Administrative organization.

Canonisation   A declaration that a person is to be made a saint or to be regarded as holy.

Chivalry   The code of conduct expected of the ideal knight.

Classical   Related to, or characteristic of, the Greeks and Romans and their civilization.

Dynasty   Ruling family.

Episcopacy   The institution of bishops.

Excommunicate   To cut off from the Church.

Fiefs   Fees or property given to vassals for their maintenance by their lords in return for service.

Feudalism   The social and legal system in which vassals were protected and maintained by lords, provided they fulfilled conditions, such as serving the lord in times of war.

Gangrenous   The death and decay of tissue due to interrupted blood supply because of injury or disease.

Gargoyle   Carved gutter spout.

Habit   The customary dress of a nun or monk.

Hierarchy   Pyramid of organization.

Illiterate   Unable to read or write.

Incumbent   A person holding an office or position.

Infidel   An unbeliever.

Inheritance   Wealth or position received through the death of another.

Interdict   The exclusion of people from certain religious services which give specific grace to the recipients.

Investiture   The formal giving of a right to possess a fief or other benefit.

Lance   A long wooden weapon with a sharp metal tip at one end.

Layman   A person who is not of the clergy.

Lymph nodes   Numerous bean-shaped masses of tissues, which help to protect the body against infection.

Mass   A major church service; the communion service.

Mercenaries   Soldiers who fight for money, rather than honour or duty.

Misericord   A ledge which projects from the underside of a hinged seat.

Obsolete   Out of date.

Papal schism   The division of the papacy between Rome and Avignon.

Principality   Country or state.

Proclaim   Announce.

Quadrivium   The higher division of the liberal arts: arithmetic, geometry, astronomy and music.

Ransom   Money paid to free a prisoner.

Remission   Forgiveness; the act of not carrying out a punishment.

Secular   Not in the Church.

Serf   An unfree person, bound to work and live on a lord's land.

Theology   The study of Christian revelation concerning God's purpose and nature.

Tracery   A pattern of interlacing ribs in the upper part of a Gothic window.

Trivium   The lower division of the seven liberal arts: grammar, rhetoric and logic.

Usurp   To take over a position of power by force.

Vassal   A man who would publicly respect and honour his lord in return for service.

Vernacular   The commonly spoken language of a particular people or place.

DATE CHART

325   Roman Emperor Constantine adopts Christianity.

354–430   The life of St Augustine, a great Christian philosopher.

406–9   Vandals invade France and Spain.

410   Rome sacked by barbarians.

c. 540   The birth of St Benedict, the founder of the Benedictine order of monks.

565   St Columba founds a monastery on the Scottish island of Iona.

570   Birth of Muhammad, founder of Islam.

590   Birth of Gregory the Great, who became Pope.

635   The Arab Empire is founded.

732 The Battle of Poitiers, where Charles Martel, grandfather of Charlemagne, defeated
the Arabs.

768–814 Reign of Charles I, called Charlemagne, King of the Franks.

793 First Viking raids in Normandy, France.

878 Vikings in the Mediterranean.

1066 Norman conquest of England.

1071 Capture of Jerusalem by the Turks.

1075–1122 Popes and emperors struggle over church appointments.

1095–9 First Crusade.

c. 1150 Beginnings of Oxford and Paris Universities.

1170 Murder of Archbishop Thomas Becket at
Canterbury.

1180–1223 Philip II (Augustus) King of France.

1182 The birth of St Francis, founder of the Franciscan order of Friars.

1187 Turkish leader Saladin recaptures Jerusalem from the Christians.

1189–92 Third Crusade led by Richard the Lionheart.

1204 Fourth Crusade; the sack of Constantinople.

1212 Children's Crusade.

1215 The barons of England force King John to sign the Magna Carta.

1226–70 The reign of Louis IX of France who was known as St Louis.

1255–69 Marco Polo travels across Asia to China.

1305–78 The papacy is exiled to Avignon, France.

1320 Birth of John Wycliffe, an English reformer of the Church.

1337 Start of one hundred years war between France and England.

1340–1400 The life of Geoffrey Chaucer, English writer and poet.

1346 Battle of Crecy; Edward III of England defeats the French and
their allies.

1347–50 The Black Death.

1357–8 Jacquerie (Peasant Revolt) in France.

1378–1417 The papal schism.

1381 Peasants' Revolt in England led by
Wat Tyler.

1412 The birth of Joan of Arc, who led France in battle against England.

1415 Execution of the preacher John Huss, who led an armed revolt against both the pope and
Emperor.

c. 1450 Printing begins to be used in Germany.

1453 Turks capture Constantinople. End of Hundred Years War; English driven from France.

1492 Columbus discovers America.

1497–9 Vasco da Gama discovers a sea route to India

1517 Martin Luther begins the Reformation.

FURTHER READING

Adams, Carol *From Workshop to Warfare—The Lives of Medieval Women* Cambridge, 1984

Aston, Margaret *The Fifteenth Century Prospect of Europe* Thames and Hudson, 1968

Barraclough, Geoffrey *The Medieval Papacy* Thames and Hudson, 1968

Bishop, Morris *The Penguin Book of the Middle Ages* Penguin, 1971

Brooke, Christopher *Europe in the Central Middle Ages* Longman, 1975

Brooke, Christopher *The Structure of Medieval Society* Thames and Hudson, 1971

Burke, John *Life in the Castle in Medieval England* Batsford, 1978

Cootes, R. J. *The Middle Ages* Longman, 1978

Gilbert, John *Knights of the Crusades* MacDonald, 1978

Hale, J. R. *Renaissance Europe 1480–1520* Fontana, 1971

Harris, Nathaniel *Spotlight on Renaissance Europe* Wayland, 1986

Hay, Denys *Europe in the Fourteenth and Fifteenth Centuries* Longman, 1970

Heer, Friedrich *The Medieval World* Cardinal, 1974

Hollister, C. W. *Medieval Europe: a Short Sourcebook* Wiley, 1982

Holmes, G. A. *Europe: Hierarchy and Revolt 1320–1450* Fontana, 1975

Jones, A. H. *The Decline of the Ancient World* Longman, 1966

Matthew, Donald *Atlas of Medieval Europe* Phaidon, 1983

Mundy, John *Europe in the High Middle Ages* 1150–1309 Longman, 1975

Saul, Nigel *The Batsford Companion to Medieval England* Batsford, 1983

Trevor-Roper, Hugh *The Rise of Christian Europe* Thames and Hudson, 1965

Picture Acknowledgements

The illustrations in this book were supplied by: BBC Hulton Picture Library 7, 13, 68, 71; The British Museum 18, 19, 21, 23, 24, 26, 58; Mary Evans Picture Library 4, 5, 9, 16, 27, 29, 37, 38, 39, 40, 41, 49, 50, 51, 52, 55, 56, 65, 66; The Mansell Collection 11, 15, 17, 20, 22, 25, 30, 44, 45, 46; John Topham 57, 61, 62, 70; Wayland Picture Library *front cover*, 6, 10, 12, 26, 28, 33, 34, 35, 36, 43, 47, 48, 54, 60, 63.

INDEX

GEORGIAN EDINBURGH

GEORGIAN EDINBURGH

IAN G. LINDSAY

O.B.E., R.S.A., F.R.I.B.A., F.R.I.A.S.

Revised by

DAVID WALKER

SCOTTISH ACADEMIC PRESS
EDINBURGH AND LONDON
1973

Published by
Scottish Academic Press Ltd
25 Perth Street, Edinburgh 3
and distributed by
Chatto & Windus Ltd
40 William IV Street
London W.C.2

*

Clarke, Irwin & Co. Ltd.,
Toronto

FIRST PUBLISHED 1948
REVISED EDITION 1973

ISBN 0 7011 1692 7

© Mrs I. G. Lindsay 1948
and David Walker 1973

PRINTED IN SCOTLAND BY
R. AND R. CLARK LTD., EDINBURGH

CONTENTS

ACKNOWLEDGMENTS

Of the numerous people to whom the author is much indebted for information and advice, particular acknowledgment must be made to Mr. E. J. MacRae, formerly City Architect, Dr. C. A. Malcolm, Mr. R. G. Cant, and the staff of the Edinburgh Room of the Public Library.

The photographs were specially taken for the work, and thanks are due to Mr. Paul Shillabeer for numbers 2, 3, 4, 6, 7, 8, 9, 10, 11, 13, 14, 15, 16, 20, 23, 24, and to Mr. Walter Scott for numbers 1, 5, 12, 17, 18, 19, 21, 22.

The line blocks were all drawn by Mr. George Hay and were based on surveys from the collection of the National Buildings Record (Scottish Council).

The picture on the jacket is taken from a steel engraving dated 1829 in *Edinburgh in the Nineteenth Century*. The view is from the east end of Princes Street looking along Waterloo Place. The Register House is on the extreme left, while opposite stands the Theatre Royal on the site of the present General Post Office. On the Calton Hill may be seen the Nelson Monument and the National Monument, the latter still surrounded by scaffolding.

INTRODUCTION

EDINBURGH is a curious place and it has a strange history. The Old Town upon its high ridge, culminating in the Castle upon its rock at one end and sinking gradually through the Canongate to the Palace on low ground at the other end, represents the capital of a medieval kingdom. This old town is possibly one of the most historic in Europe and it still retains the trappings of its former dignity, its great church, its palace, its fortress, its parliament house, the meeting-place of its city fathers and its university. But the backbone which supported these institutions is nearly gone, for the old dwellings of the people of high and low degree are but scantily represented. Here and there are ancient houses of great merit, but those which have been kept in reasonable repair can almost be counted on the fingers of one hand. This is a most deplorable state of affairs which would not be tolerated in most countries. Thus the old town, in spite of its history, which doesn't necessarily interest everybody, cannot afford to rest on its laurels much longer if anyone, except the paper historian, is going to enjoy it in the future. Such old houses as remain must be retained. It doesn't matter a bit who did or did not live in them in the past, for they are much better in themselves as examples of the solid architecture and craftsmanship of their period than many which are the boast of other European capitals.

So much for the Old Town; but there is also a New Town which is one of the most remarkable achievements of the late 18th and early 19th centuries, an amazing development which produced miles of streets and numerous public buildings, squares and terraces without parallel in their period. However, because there is so much of the

New Town, it does not mean that it should be wantonly hacked about as was the Old Town in the past or merely allowed to decay like the Old Town at present. In fact even less so, for it is a matter of streets and not of individual houses. The streets were designed as a whole, the houses are merely subordinate parts of a general scheme, and the alteration or removal of a single house in such places as Charlotte Square, Great King Street, Moray Place or Melville Street would wreck the whole effect of the symmetry which is the essence of these streets. Much damage has already been done, for the astragals have often been removed from the windows and plate glass substituted, thus upsetting the scale, and extra floors or unsightly dormers have been added above the cornice thus destroying, not only the elevation of the house concerned, but the balance of the whole street. Nevertheless except in George Street and Princes Street there has been comparatively little wholesale destruction of the actual buildings. It is therefore to be hoped in this age when everything is planned, or is supposed to be planned, that the planning of a previous age may be respected and furthermore with this example before them it may even be possible, should they be humble enough, for the present-day planners to learn just a little, not only of the possibilities but of the limitations of planning.

So this small book has been compiled as a modest introduction to the rather neglected subject of the Georgian architecture of Edinburgh, an essentially Georgian city. May it remind the citizen who daily walks the pavements of the Modern Athens that there is something to be seen around him and may it give the stranger, who crosses the North Sea or the Atlantic to view the Athenian squares and terraces, some slight information which otherwise he certainly will not obtain without considerable trouble.

For convenience the term Georgian has been taken very literally, and this account only includes buildings

erected between the accession of George I in 1714 and
the death of George IV in 1830. This does not mean
that this particular architectural style began or ended on
these dates, for in fact very little was done during the
reigns of the first two Hanoverians. The sixty years during
which George III occupied the throne saw an ever-increasing impetus in building, and this went on till long after
1830. The advent of the railways during the 1840's marked
the end of an orderly development throughout the city as
a whole but, in certain quarters, street planning on " Georgian " lines, though lacking the Georgian elegance of taste,
was carried on till the early years of the present century.

In general layout the book follows on the lines of its
predecessor *Old Edinburgh*. The endpaper map is a
reference plan to the position of the buildings detailed in
the text. Each church, in the list or on the map, is marked
by a Roman numeral, each public building by an Arabic
figure, and each planning area or district by a capital letter.
For further classification the successive " New Towns " are
variously cross hatched. In the text each type of building
is arranged in chronological order, and the descriptions
are purposely short, for they are intended for use on the
spot rather than for study at a distance. A note on some
of the architects who produced these buildings and who
laid out the streets is also included. Only a few of these
men are well known, but it is impossible to understand
the development of the city without at least a knowledge
of their names. For instance certain people, sometimes
those who should know much better, imagine that Craig
was responsible for the whole town, while others have an
idea that Adam designed most of it.

EDITOR'S NOTE TO THE SECOND EDITON

Shortly before Ian Lindsay died in 1966, he discussed
with me a revised edition for which he had made many
notes based on his own further researches and the work

Miss Catherine Cruft and I had carried out under his supervision for the Scottish Office. He intended to rewrite the chapter on the streets and houses completely and make some amendments, mainly of opinion rather than fact, in the others. Since his death Professor A. J. Youngson's *The Making of Classical Edinburgh* has contributed much to our knowledge of Georgian Edinburgh, particularly in respect of how it was built and financed. To it the reader who wishes to pursue the subject in greater depth is referred.

Ian Lindsay's book still has its place. It is concise and compact, and contains a goodly number of architectural facts not to be found in Youngson's. Since his text is still as valid as when first written, we have thought it best to leave his text as he wrote it with only a few minor amendments which extended knowledge and subsequent events have made necessary. The only major change is at page 29. Since the book had to be completely reset we have taken the opportunity of expanding his brief account of David Bryce and his successors. Rather than re-write the last chapter we have added appendices giving the additional details he would have included in it had he lived to do so.

A great deal of Ian Lindsay's pleading for the preservation of the old and new towns may seem irrelevant now. Since 1948 the old town has been partially restored, sometimes into something rather different from the original, and partially demolished. The importance of conserving the New Town has been accepted by the City and the Government alike and the New Town Conservation Committee set up. In creating the informed climate of opinion which made this possible Ian Lindsay's little book played no small part and his words are now of historical interest in themselves.

DAVID WALKER
January 1973

THE GEORGIAN DEVELOPMENT

WHEN George I ascended the throne of Great Britain in 1714, Scotland was exceedingly depressed as a result of the unpopular Union of the Parliaments seven years previously, and Edinburgh, as the capital city, was more affected than any other part of the country. It had been bad enough when the Court moved to England in 1603, but the departure of the Parliament as well, with all it involved, stripped the town of every vestige of its former dignity, of its trade and of its future. The Union had been initiated from England, largely by the fear of what an independent Scottish Parliament might do regarding the succession to the throne on the death of Queen Anne, for there was no reason why it should necessarily accept a member of the House of Hanover. The Act had been pushed through from the south in a manner which had been deeply resented by the Scottish people, and they could see no redeeming feature in such a one-sided bargain. Nor, in fact, was there. Hence it is hardly surprising that the first event in Georgian Scotland was the " Rising " in 1715.

This depression was naturally reflected in the state of the town itself and had much to do with its very retarded development compared with places which had not tasted the degradation of tne Scottish capital. In 1714 the city was still contained within its ancient Royalty which extended to the surprisingly small area of 138 acres and which, roughly, was still bounded by the walls built after the battle of Flodden, two hundred years before. This patch of land was grossly overcrowded, as the population was probably at least 25,000 and, in places, buildings towered twelve storeys above the streets. Even so, little or no improvement in these conditions was to start for another fifty years. There were certainly some natural disadvantages. The city stood on a high ridge. All expansion to the west was blocked by the Castle, and to the east by the burgh of Canongate, while the low ground to the north was filled by the Nor' Loch and on the south the Burgh Loch, on the site of the Meadows, had not yet been drained.

But the unsettled state of the country also hindered development, and it was not till after the decisive defeat of the Jacobite Rising in 1746 that there was much talk of city improvements. Only a few new buildings had been erected in this first period. New Greyfriars Kirk (by Alex McGill in the tradition of the previous century) was tacked on to the ruined west end of the old kirk in 1721, James' Court was founded on the north side of the Lawnmarket by a builder, named James Brownhill, in 1725, and achieved a little more light and air than was then common in the town, while in 1738 the foundation stone of the Infirmary was laid. This building, designed by William Adam senior, has now been demolished, but its pediment may still be seen, rebuilt on ground level at Redford.

In 1752 resolutions were drawn up by the Town Council to effect certain improvements, some of which had already been suggested in the time of the Stuarts, seventy years before. One, which was defeated, was an extension of the Royalty over the fields to the north, and another was the building of a Royal Exchange, which went on, the foundation stone being laid the following year. Meanwhile some small squares had been erected to the south of the town by local builders, Argyll Square about 1746 and Alison Square in 1750. These were followed by a third, Brown Square, in 1763. They were very small and as squares have vanished, but a great advance was the layout of George Square in 1766 by James Brown " a wright and architect ", who named it after his brother George. This speculation was the first scheme of any size (660 feet × 500 feet), and in fact it still remains one of the largest spaces of its kind in the city. The houses are not uniform, but they adhere to a general height and scale. Being outside the Royalty, the square was regarded as a suburb, but nevertheless it had certain solid advantages as dues levied within the town did not affect it.

A small scheme of the same period was the formation, at right angles to the Canongate, of St. John's Street which was building in 1768. Almost all of this street of plain, self-contained houses has now vanished.

The more official plans were meanwhile going ahead. The public-spirited Lord Provost, George Drummond, who since 1724 had been urging extensions to the north and who had sponsored the Infirmary and the 1752 improvements, was still endeavouring to extend the Royalty, but realised that nothing much would be done till there was access to the proposed ground on the far side of the Nor' Loch valley. Accordingly in 1763 the North Bridge was begun, without saying overmuch about extension, but with considerable advertisement regarding a new road to Leith. This was a clever move, for by 1767 Parliament passed an Act empowering an extension of the Royalty to an area of 192 acres over the fields where George Street and Princes Street now stand. The previous year the Town Council had organised a competition for the layout of their New Town, and this was won by a young architect, named James Craig, who was awarded a gold medal and the freedom of the city in a silver box. On 26th October, 1767, Craig laid, in Rose Court, the foundation stone of the first house. Some persuasion was necessary to induce people to build on so wind-swept and lonely a spot, and matters were not improved by part of the new North Bridge collapsing in 1769, when it was nearly finished. However, within the next few years a real start was made, and the new site was pretty well covered by the end of the century.

Craig's plan has had many critics, but certain points must be remembered. His town was designed as a residential, self-contained suburb, not as the business centre it now is. Hence the principal street, George Street, on the top of the ridge, was closed at each end by a square. Further expansion was deemed utterly fantastic, so neither of these squares was provided with direct east or west access to the surrounding country. The two other principal streets were designed as terraces, Princes Street, looking south to the Old Town and to the Castle (over what was to have been a canal but is now the railway), and Queen Street, looking north over the fields to the Firth of Forth and Fife. Though the plan intended Princes Street to be open to the south, the temptation to build there grew so strong that houses were actually begun, and an Act had to be passed to prevent further such activities for all time coming. Narrow streets " for shopkeepers and others " run between and parallel to the above-mentioned thoroughfares, while behind them are mewses.

To begin with, the houses, like those of George Square, were not necessarily uniform. Strict regulations regarding height and so forth had to be observed, but individuals could take feus of any frontage they desired, provided, of course, that due care was taken to leave a proper house width when the end of the block was reached. This arrangement may still be seen on the north side of St. Andrew Square and in Queen Street. The first effort to treat a block of houses as a whole was in Charlotte Square, the western extremity of the town. Designs for this square were prepared by Robert Adam in 1791 but, after his death during the following year, the Town Council allowed various deviations from his plans, and the alterations to the east and west sides were particularly unfortunate. Also, to all intents and purposes, they scrapped Adam's design for the church which was to close the New Town vista on the west, substituting one by Robert Reid, which was carried out by 1814 and which was not of the same architectural standard as that previously intended.

While the New Town was being built, further extensions and improvements were begun to the south of the Old Town. An Act was passed in 1785 authorising the construction of the South Bridge and the erection of a new University building. The South Bridge spans the Cowgate Valley in a series of nineteen arches, only one of which is visible, and is in direct line with the North Bridge, the road between them crossing the old High Street at right angles. The bridge was finished in 1788 and in November 1789 the foundation stone of the University was laid. However, owing to lack of funds, work ceased before the building was half-finished, and when it was resumed again in 1815, Robert Adam, who had prepared the designs, was dead. So once again his work was interfered with by a later hand.

The southern suburbs beyond the South Bridge and its extension Nicolson Street grew in rather a haphazard fashion. Several small squares and new streets were built, but they were fitted into an earlier development which had grown up along the medieval road system leading from the south to the ports or gateways in the town wall.

The last thirty years of the period, the first thirty of the 19th century, saw an immense increase in building, and several notable schemes were executed in Edinburgh before the advent of the railways and the Industrial Revolution upset the equilibrium and resulted in the mediocre belt which surrounds the city.

With the layout of the ground immediately to the north of Queen Street Gardens by Reid and Sibbald in 1802, a second New Town was created. In conception it is somewhat similar to its predecessor—a wide street running east and west (Great King Street) with open spaces at either end. Looking south, Heriot Row and Abercrombie Place, the latter being the first curved street façade in Edinburgh,

and looking to the North, Fettes Row and Royal Crescent.
Between them are narrower streets and mewses. One great
difference from the first New Town was, however, that
each block was treated as a single architectural composition,
and the houses had, as in Charlotte Square, to conform.
Another difference is that the main street lies half-way
down a hill, not along the top of a ridge as does George
Street, and the traffic routes cross the area from south to
north ; hence the conception of the plan which looks very
well on paper is not so obvious in fact.

Next, in 1812, a competition was advertised for the
layout of the Calton Hill and ground to the north thereof,
bounded on the west by Leith Walk. However, the
assessor's reports on the plans of the thirty-two competitors
seem to have shaken the authorities so much that they
accepted none of them and in 1818 gave the job to Playfair.
Even then, long delays led to the final breakdown of the
whole scheme. The great terraces on the hill (Royal,
Carlton, and Regent) were eventually completed though,
even in 1852, only half Royal Terrace had been erected.
Below, the western end of Hillside Crescent was built
and parts of the streets radiating from it, but the rest of
the proposed area is now occupied by railway goods yards
and factories.

In 1815 Robert Stevenson planned the eastern access
to Princes Street round the Calton Hill, an operation
necessitating the blasting of a considerable amount of
rock, cutting through the Old Calton Burying Ground
and bridging the deep glen which divided the hill from
the New Town. Three sets of plans were submitted for
the architectural adornment of this approach and those of
Archibald Elliot were chosen. The result was good ;
Ionic porticos face Princes Street on either side of Waterloo
Place as, at that date, the western end of the new approach
could not fail to be named. The Ionic screens on either
side of the Regent Bridge are a fitting link to the buildings

forming the street, and farther east, the Doric walls which decently shroud all but the most important monuments of the old burial ground, were an admirable introduction to the rough hillside on one side and the battlemented towers of Elliot's toy fort jail on the other. The Jail, though in such a different style, was also founded in 1815 but has since been removed, except for the picturesque Governor's House perched on a rugged crag. Its place has been taken by a large modern structure of international design through which London transmits its instructions to the Scottish Nation.

The Calton Hill itself was not forgotten, though in 1815 it was still in a reasonably natural state. At the summit was a small observatory, started in 1776 by James Craig, with advice from Robert Adam on how best to make it appear like a fortification. In 1807, the inevitable happened and the observatory was joined by a Nelson Monument, the last building near the summit of the hill, in the romantic manner, for by this time Edinburgh had begun to see herself as a northern reflection of ancient Athens and took the illusion pretty seriously. To the Modern Athenians, the Calton Hill seemed to be an admirable Acropolis. That this was so there could be little doubt, for all travellers who had been to Greece told them so ; in fact the Calton was a bit higher, and quite probably rather finer than the original. Thus in 1818 Playfair started a new observatory with no fewer than four porticos, and set at a corner of its boundary wall a heavy Doric memorial to his uncle. Four years later the foundation stone of a full-size reproduction of the Parthenon, by C. R. Cockerell, was laid, to grow into a National Monument commemorating the late wars, a pious hope never to be fulfilled, for only twelve columns were built. Another three years and Thomas Hamilton was starting his superb High School, a little bit down the hill, to designs borrowed from the Theseion. Then in 1830 and 1831, both he and Playfair tried out their own variation of the Choragic Monument of Lysicrates on jutting crags, one in memory of Robert Burns, the other of Dugald Stewart.

This Grecian ardour was not, of course, to be confined to the rocks of the Calton, and all over the town porticos, pilasters and pediments sprang up. Almost every street was adorned with Greek detail of some kind, and, though there was no Pentelic marble at hand, these works were all executed in most excellent stone which could be cut to the finest detail with great precision. The new Edinburgh was most fortunate in having this admirable material at her gates in the shape of the calciferous sandstone obtained from the quarries of Craigleith, Barnton, Ravelston and Hailes. The first named is especially famous and, apart from its extensive use in Edinburgh, it was much exported. Parts of the old Bank of England, the British Museum, and Buckingham Palace, all in London, were built of it. From the Hailes Quarry came most of the paving stones for the city.

Shortly after 1813, still another New Town was begun beyond the west end of Princes Street, which was to form the western approach from Glasgow. The main road leaves the town after traversing two shallow crescents (Atholl and Coates), though the main axis of this scheme is Melville Street which runs parallel a little to the north. Further streets were projected beyond this, but were not to be carried out for another eighty years ; broadly on the original layout but most certainly not adhering to the same type of elevation or detail.

The last scheme of any size to be erected during the Georgian era filled a gap at the north-west corner of the original New Town with the Water of Leith Valley to the north and Reid and Sibbald's Second New Town to the east. This land belonged to the Earl of Moray, and the streets, laid out by Gillespie Graham after 1822, bear the names of the Moray family or of their estates. The main axis lies at an angle of about 45 degrees across the corner of Craig's plan and consists of a crescent, an oval and a polygon cleverly connected by short lengths of street to the stray ends of the two earlier schemes. The impressive elevations are rather heavy but, to quote a contemporary writer, were " designed to contain the residences of the magnates of Edinburgh, whose fate it is, every few years to be expelled from their appropriate districts by the intrusion of the trading classes."

Though Telford's Dean Bridge was not finished till 1831, to open the Learmonth estate, as well as to provide more direct access to Queensferry, building had nevertheless been started on the far side of the Water of Leith some years earlier by Sir Henry Raeburn, the portrait painter. The feuing of his lands resulted in the imposing St. Bernard's Crescent and the charming little Ann Street, named after his wife.

Such, in broad outline, was the development of Edinburgh during the Georgian period. The first fifty years was a period of depression and stagnation, the next thirty-five a time of experiment and a careful issuing from the Old Town, while the last thirty years were marked by a too rapid growth which was, in part, responsible for its downfall. It will be noted that after Craig's plan there has been no mention of accommodation " for shopkeepers and others." In fact there wasn't any or very little. So what with their ever-increasing requirements, the over-building of large houses, the advent of railways and the coming of the machine, the whole system broke down very suddenly, as can be clearly observed in many places where fine terraces cease abruptly, to merge into a series of shacks, a garage or a factory. However, within this perimeter, Edinburgh still remains very much as it was when George IV was gathered to his ancestors.

THE ARCHITECTS

FOUR years before the opening of the Georgian period, Sir William Bruce of Kinross died. He was the first man in Scotland who could claim to have been an architect in anything like the modern sense of the word. An old man, he was a link with a remote past, for this staunch adherent of the Stuarts must well have remembered the days of Charles I. He designed the last palace of that ill-fated race, Holyroodhouse, and was largely responsible for the introduction of a developed renaissance architecture to Scotland. It is generally supposed that William Adam senior worked under him. The latter certainly continued the work at Hopetoun after Bruce's death, but, as he himself died in 1748 during the dark age in Edinburgh, he cannot be expected to have contributed much to the buildings of the city. He was, however, responsible for the old Infirmary founded in 1738, at which date his famous son Robert was a child of ten.

Robert Adam was born in Kirkcaldy, and on his return from his enterprising tour in 1758 took London by storm. He had gone beyond Rome to the Dalmatian coast, and came back full of the Palace of Diocletian at Spalatro, whose glories he lost no time in publishing by means of a great book illustrated with engravings by Piranesi and Bartolozzi. Not only that, but, with the production of a light and brilliant detail, he applied new forms, which cut through the tediously correct Palladianism of the day as practised by such architects as Vardy and Flitcroft. Though he continued to work from London, he left his mark in Edinburgh, both by the buildings he erected and by a rather short-lived influence. The most complete of his larger buildings is the Register House started in 1774, but had the University, founded in 1789, been finished by him it would have been by far the finest. Charlotte Square, designed in 1791, the year before his death, was also considerably altered some years later during its construction, and the strange St. George's Episcopal Chapel in the Gothic style, for which Adam drawings exist, was not built till 1794, so it was probably designed by his younger brother James. Robert certainly built No. 8 Queen Street, and probably designed or advised upon several other houses in Queen Street and George Street. Robert, though the most famous, was one of four brothers. John the eldest (1721-92) was not so concerned with affairs in the south and spent part of his time in Edinburgh managing the business of the firm in Scotland and part running the family estate at Blair Adam in Kinross-shire James (1730-94) did many of the drawings, and William (1738-1822) was chiefly concerned with financial matters. The Adam tradition had a considerable influence upon Craig's New Town and many of the houses contain " Adam " mantelpieces, at least ninety-five per cent. of which were productions of the joiners' copy books of the period and never emanated from the Albemarle Street office. This influence did not last very long, however, for it was swept away by the Greek phase of the early nineteenth century, a phase which was even more studiously correct than the Palladian of the mid-eighteenth.

Another family of architects belonging to the earlier period was that of Mylne, who were hereditary Royal Master Masons. The first of the line was John, Master Mason to James III, who died in the early 16th century. The eighth in succession, and first to call himself an architect, was William who died in 1728 and was followed by his son Thomas, surveyor to the city. He had two sons who were the contemporaries of the Adam Brethren, Robert being born in 1733 and William in 1734. These brothers also went on tour, and Robert won the Papal medal at the

Academy of St. Luke in Rome in 1758. He returned, to
London, shortly afterwards and won the competition for
Blackfriars Bridge. Thereafter most of his practice was in
England, though he was responsible for St. Cecilia's Hall in
Niddrie Street (1762). He later became surveyor to St.
Paul's Cathedral, London, and after his death in 1811 was
buried there. William's career was not so brilliant. He
designed the old North Bridge, and naturally got into some
trouble when a large part of it fell down in 1769, with loss
of life, just before it was finished. He ended his days in
1790 as engineer to the Waterworks in Dublin, and thus the
Mylne family went furth of Scotland.

Other names of the mid 18th century are rather undis-
tinguished, and the authors of the earlier " improvements "
were really speculative builders, such as James Brownhill
who erected James Court in 1725 and called it after himself,
and James Brown who built Brown Square and later George
Square. John Baxter, who designed the Merchants' Hall in
1788 and carried out work at Gordon Castle, was also
responsible for remodelling the Tron Kirk in 1785-7.

James Craig, the winner of the New Town competition,
who was born in 1744, definitely had an architectural
training for he was a pupil of Sir Robert Taylor in London.
His name will certainly be remembered in connection with
the layout of the New Town, but his buildings do not
appear to have been very brilliant and his best, the
Physicians' Hall in George Street, was pulled down over
a hundred years ago. He died in 1795, before his New
Town was completed.

A name which is apt to crop up in unexpected places
till well into the 19th century is that of Alexander Nasmyth
(1758-1840). He came of a family who had been builders
in the town for several generations, and his father, Michael,
built much of George Square, some of St. Andrew Square,
and other houses in the New Town. Alexander took up
painting, studied under Allan Ramsay and set up as a

portrait painter, but later he deserted this and turned to landscape. However he did many other things. His association with Miller of Dalswinton led to his dabbling in early steam boats and cannon. He laid out parks, altered houses and built rustic bridges for the nobility and gentry. He was a competitor in the Calton layout scheme of 1812, produced extensive designs for the Nelson and National Monuments which were not carried out, and otherwise advised upon improvements. St. Bernard's Well (1789) is rather typical of his work, a charming contribution to the picturesque. His son, James, is possibly better known, for he was the inventor of the steam hammer.

Thomas Telford was born in Eskdale the year before Nasmyth and as a young man worked as a stone mason in the New Town. Though he migrated to London, the great engineer was often in Scotland directing his road works, the Caledonian Canal and numerous other undertakings. In Edinburgh he reported on the water supply in 1813 from data produced by James Jardine, the ingenious engineer who designed the very subtle heating of the Signet Library. Telford's most notable work in the town is the Dean Bridge (1829-31).

Four years later, in 1761, John Rennie was born in East Lothian, but he also went to London. He designed Leith Docks in 1800, and later he, Telford, and Hugh Baird all produced different lines for the course of the Union Canal between Edinburgh and the Forth and Clyde Canal at Falkirk. Baird (1770-1827) eventually was given the work which was started in 1818.

One more engineer should be noted before returning to architects and that is Robert Stevenson (1772-1850). Though he is chiefly known for the construction of lighthouses, including the famous Bell Rock, he was responsible for the layout of the eastern approach to Princes Street round the south side of the Calton Hill in 1815.

The remaining architects are those who fashioned the

Athenian phase of the Regency and reign of George IV.
The eldest was Archibald Elliot, born in 1761. His best-
known works are very varied in style though close in date :
1815 produced the designs of Waterloo Place, Regent
Bridge and the Calton Jail ; 1816 the old County Hall,
an Ionic structure, now demolished, and St. Paul's Episcopal Chapel in English Perpendicular.

William Stark was really a Glasgow man, but moved to
Edinburgh for health reasons towards the end of his days
and there designed the fine interior of the Signet Library.
He was involved in the Calton layout competition, but died
in 1813 before his report on the plans of the various competitors was finished. Enough of it was written, however,
to influence the Town Council against going on at the time.

A person who considered himself of some importance
at this period was Robert Reid, who was born in 1776
and who became the last King's Architect or Master of
the King's Works for Scotland, an office which was abolished
in 1840. His work was apt to be rather heavy ; for instance,
his design for St. George's Church did not appreciate the
delicate scale of Charlotte Square, nor is his Parliament
Square very inspiring. He thought that he should have
been given the University to finish, and on that account
would not enter for the competition, but, as far as Adam
work is concerned, he did complete the Register House.
Nevertheless some of his street elevations in the Second
New Town, such as those of Great King Street and Drummond Place, have undoubted merit. Also his later work at
St. Andrews in a free Jacobean style is rather pleasing. He
died in 1856.

James Gillespie, son of the Sheriff of Dunblane, was born
in 1776. He trained first as a wright, but in due course had
the good sense to marry an heiress in Margaret Anne,
daughter of William Graham of Orchil. Thereafter he
became James Gillespie Graham and the great champion
of the early romantic Gothic revival in Scotland. He built

PLATE I

ST. ANDREW'S AND ST. GEORGE'S CHURCH   STEEPLE, W. SIBBALD, 1789

PLATE 2

ST. MARY'S CHURCH   T. BROWN, 1824

PLATE 3

ST. JOHN'S EPISCOPAL CHAPEL　　　　　　　　W. BURN, 1816

PLATE 4

THE ROYAL EXCHANGE

PLATE 5

THE REGISTER HOUSE   R. ADAM, begun 1774

PLATE 6

THE SIGNET LIBRARY   W. STARK, completed R. REID, 1812–13

PLATE 7

THE UNIVERSITY LIBRARY
W. H. PLAYFAIR, 1816–17

PLATE 8

THE UNIVERSITY

R. ADAM, 1789

numerous turreted and pinnacled mansions throughout the country, some of which, such as the new Castle at Murthly show a good sense of composition. He latterly collaborated in several works with A. W. N. Pugin (1812-52), the most notable being the Tolbooth Church with its fine spire. His earliest building in Edinburgh was the Roman Catholic Chapel (now Cathedral) in 1813 ; a similar church followed the next year in Glasgow, and in 1819 he built Dr. Jamieson's Chapel in Nicolson Street. All have a distinct family resemblance and were the first examples of Gothic facades fitted into classic street elevations and which were to become so popular. One of his few essays in the classic manner was the layout of the Moray estate in 1822. Here he does not seem to have been very sure of his detail, which shows a remarkable sameness throughout the scheme. He died in 1855.

The next in order was Thomas Hamilton, who was born in Edinburgh in 1784, the son of a carpenter and builder to whom he was apprenticed. His architectural career started in 1818 when he won the competition for the Burns Monument at Alloway, and from then till his death in 1858 his practice was extensive. His greatest work in Edinburgh is undoubtedly the Royal High School (1825) on the Calton Hill. In 1830 he designed the Burns Monument nearby and laid out George IV Bridge and Johnston Terrace in 1827. The neo-baroque Dean Orphanage followed in 1831 and the neo-Greek Royal College of Physicians in 1845. Though he occasionally used the Gothic style for churches, his work was essentially classical, of which manner he had a great command of detail besides a fine sense of composition.

1789 is notable as the year in which were born both William Henry Playfair and William Burn, while the following year gave Archibald Simpson, whose work in Aberdeen affords a most interesting comparison with that of the Edinburgh men. This trio were competent architects and all had large practices. Playfair was the son of a Scottish architect, James Playfair, who worked in London though he returned annually to Scotland to supervise the various country houses upon which he was engaged. In 1794, James died, and his son came to live with his uncle, Professor John Playfair, in Edinburgh, where he was apprenticed to William Stark. Later he returned to London for a spell in the offices of Smirke and Wyatt, made a short tour of France and returned to Edinburgh in time to win the competition for the completion of Robert Adam's University. In 1818 he built the New Observatory on the Calton Hill, and in the following year laid out the great terraces on the east side of the hill, together with the low ground on the north. With the foundation of the National Monument in 1822, his Greek phase intensified and was to produce the Royal Institution on the Mound, the Surgeons' Hall (1832), the Dugald Stewart Monument (1831) and, towards the end of his career, the National Gallery in 1850. His work, however, was not entirely classical, though such varied buildings as Donaldson's Hospital and the New College belong to the Victorian era. He died in 1857.

William Burn also had an architectural background, for his father, Robert Burn, was an architect whose best known, and much criticised, work was the Nelson Monument on the Calton Hill. In 1808 he was, like Playfair, sent to London and also to the office of Robert Smirke where, no doubt, he assisted with the rush job of rebuilding the Covent Garden Opera House which had been burnt down that year and which was reopened twelve months later. On his return to Edinburgh at the age of 23, his first work was the Parish Church of North Leith with a fine Ionic portico and admirable steeple. But Burn was a most versatile person and his next building, designed two years later, was the ornate Perpendicular Gothic St. John's Episcopal Chapel. With the Melville Column, Edinburgh Academy and John Watson's, he returned again to the classical, though in other places, such as at Dunfermline Abbey, Gothic was in full swing. Unfortunately one of his poorest essays in that style happened to be the renovation of the exterior of St. Giles', which was begun in 1829. His practice grew so large, particularly with country-house work, that he moved to London in 1844, leaving David Bryce in charge of his Edinburgh office. The partnership was dissolved six years later, but Burn prospered in the south till as late as 1870.

Bryce, who was born in 1803, designed some fine buildings in Edinburgh, and dotted Scotland with imposing baronial mansions during the Victorian period. He greatly enriched the original New Town. In George Street he contributed the insurance buildings at Nos. 19 and 95 (the former since altered as the George Hotel) in 1840 and the Clydesdale Bank in 1841-2. All these are in a late Georgian Graeco-Roman manner of which David Rhind's Commercial (now Royal) Bank also in George Street (1846-7) is perhaps the most memorable example. Bryce's subsequent buildings are mostly Italian renaissance and reflect the influence of Sir Charles Barry, as at 22-24 George Street (1847), the British Linen Bank (now Bank of Scotland, 1845-50) and the former Exchange Bank (1846) at No. 23 St. Andrew Square. His Western Bank, later the Scottish Widows Building (1846), in the same square has alas disappeared. The reconstruction of the Bank of Scotland (1865-70) shows him in Roman Baroque mood, but in his last work, the Union Bank (now Bank of Scotland, 1874-8), in George Street, he remained faithful to the ideals of forty years before.

Bryce is a valuable figure in the architectural succession Burn and Bryce's was a great teaching office and their influence in both plan and elevation is observed throughout the land. Many of the best Victorian architects trained there, while others such as James Maitland Wardrop (1824-1882) were deeply influenced by him. Before Bryce formed his last partnership with his nephew John, he was briefly in partnership with Sir Rowand Anderson (1834-1921). Anderson formed another partnership with Wardrop's son Hew (1856-87). In that office Sir Robert Lorimer was trained and from their offices came many of the architects working in Edinburgh today.

THE CHURCHES

As the architectural style favoured by the various denominations varies somewhat, it is convenient to divide this section into three parts. The Established Church showed a conservative leaning towards classical adornment, the Episcopalians and Roman Catholics went wholeheartedly for the Gothic revival, as might be expected, while the numerous variations of the secession and other dissenting bodies tended towards a Tuscan pilaster or two, but if even that could not be afforded, the general idea was usually towards a classic rather than a Gothic mannerism.

THE CHURCH OF SCOTLAND

The purpose of these churches was to seat a large congregation, generally at least 1,500 within a reasonable distance of the pulpit, and the resulting plan is much the same in all cases. It usually consisted of a wide rectangle with the pulpit at one end and large galleries round the remaining three walls. There was no question of the provision of a chancel or of an organ. The exterior was decently adorned on the street facade with a steeple and sometimes with a portico as well, in order to ornament the city.

NEW GREYFRIARS CHURCH   *I*

Erected in 1721 by the Town Council and paid for by a duty on ale, this church is in the 17th century tradition. It was added to the west end of Old Greyfriars Church (1614) on the site of a tower which, being used as a powder magazine, had blown up in 1718. The architect was Alexander McGill. The dividing wall was removed in 1936.

St. Andrew's Church, George Street (now St. Andrew's and St. George's) *II*

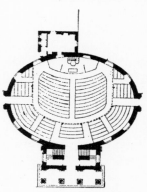

St. Andrew's Church

In Craig's plan for the New Town, a church stood in the centre of the east side of St. Andrew Square, axial with George Street, but, in fact, the proposed site was acquired for a house, and the church was relegated to the north side of George Street. It was the first church to be built in the New Town, which already had had a theatre for sixteen years, and was the subject of a competition which was won by Major Frazer of the Engineers. Started in 1785 it was completed two years later except for the steeple, which was added in 1789 by William Sibbald. The steeple was provided with a peal of six bells rung after the English fashion which caused much comment, as Scotland followed continental methods of campanology. The church itself is of oval plan and still contains its original pulpit, galleries and some of the pews.

St. Cuthbert's Steeple, Lothian Road *III*

Of medieval foundation, St. Cuthbert's formerly served an extensive country parish around the town. It was rebuilt in a plain style in 1774 and again in 1893. Only the steeple of the 18th century church remains. It was finished in 1790 and has been attributed to H. Weir, although Alexander Stevens had some hand in it.

At the kirkyard gate is a small battlemented tower, dated 1827, which provided shelter for the watchmen who were necessary at that period to prevent newly buried corpses being dug up and sold to the dissecting rooms.

LADY YESTER'S CHURCH, INFIRMARY STREET   *IV*

A mid 17th century foundation which was reopened on
a new site in 1805 and finally closed as a church in 1938.
The street facade consists of a heavy gable with pseudo-
Gothic windows.

ST. GEORGE'S CHURCH (now WEST REGISTER HOUSE),
    CHARLOTTE SQUARE   *V*

In his design for Charlotte Square, Robert Adam
included a large church in the centre of the west side but
his plan was abandoned after his death as being too
costly, and the present building was erected by Robert
Reid between 1811 and 1814. The great Ionic columns
at the entrance are rather out of scale with the square, but
the dome forms one of the main features of the New Town.
    Within, the original interior has entirely disappeared.

HOPE PARK CHAPEL (now NEWINGTON AND ST. LEONARD'S
    CHURCH)   *VI*

Built in 1823 by Robert Brown as a Chapel of Ease to
St. Cuthbert's. The street facade is treated with pilasters
and is surmounted by
a small steeple. Within
are the normal galleries
and the original pul-
pit.

CLAREMONT STREET
CHAPEL (now ST. BER-
NARD'S CHURCH) *VII*

Also built in 1823 as
a Chapel of Ease to St.
Cuthbert's by James
Milne, architect. A
simple facade with Ionic
pilasters and a steeple

CLAREMONT STREET CHAPEL

above.   The interior was rearranged and an apse added in 1888.

ST. MARY'S CHURCH, BELLEVUE CRESCENT   *VIII*

Built in 1824 by Thomas Brown, Overseer of Public Works for the city.   As the central feature of a shallow crescent, the church has an imposing Corinthian portico surmounted by a steeple.   The plan is normal and the interior retains the original pulpit.

THE TRON STEEPLE   *IX*

The Tron Kirk was founded in 1633 and built to the designs of John Mylne (1611-67), an uncle of Robert Mylne, the builder of Holyroodhouse.   It was shortened at either end and the south aisle removed in 1788 by Baxter for the South Bridge improvements scheme.   In the great fire of 1824, it lost its picturesque steeple which was replaced by the present one, designed by R. & R. Dickson in 1828.

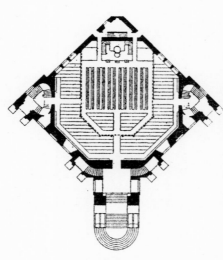

ST. STEPHEN'S CHURCH
(Original arrangement showing
Communion tables)

ST. STEPHEN'S CHURCH *X*

A curious church on a difficult site, built in 1828 by W. H Playfair. It stands at the bottom of a steep hill with the street dividing on either side of it.   The tower is on the main axis, and the body of the church forms a square, set diagonally, behind the tower. The interior, however, is octagonal and the main entrance, at the head of an imposing flight of steps, ascending through the tower under a great arch, leads, rather surprisingly, into the gallery. It is best summed up by a contemporary writer, " its style very unique, in Scotland at least."

THE SCOTTISH EPISCOPAL
AND ROMAN CATHOLIC CHURCHES

During a considerable part of the Georgian era, these denominations were profoundly suspect and laboured under penal laws. The members of the Scottish Episcopal Church, disestablished in 1689, were largely Jacobites, and, after the Rising of 1745, these laws were particularly severe. However, after the death of Prince Charles in Rome in 1788, there was no reason to continue such restrictions, and their abolition in 1792 soon led to a certain amount of building. There had been two distinct types of congregation, the Jurors (who prayed for the Hanoverians and who were not affected by the penal laws) and the non-Jurors (who prayed for the Stuarts). The Cowgate Chapel (Item XI) was, naturally enough, built by the former order.

The Roman Catholics also suffered under harsh penal laws, and such was the popular resentment against that Church that there were serious riots in Edinburgh in 1779 after the repeal of similar restrictions in England. A Relief Act was passed in 1793, which at least allowed Roman Catholics freedom of worship, though they were still excluded from most civil appointments.

THE COWGATE EPISCOPAL CHAPEL (now St. Patrick's R.C. Church) *XI*

Opened in 1774. The plan is a plain rectangle with a steeple at the southern end which, according to the original design, was to be finished with a Corinthian portico. This was never built, and the present front was added in 1928. An apse, decorated with paintings by Alexander Runciman, projects from the east side, and the remaining walls were formerly fitted with galleries.

ST. GEORGE'S EPISCOPAL CHAPEL, YORK PLACE   *XII*

By its conversion into commercial premises, this church has been so mutilated that it can scarcely qualify for inclusion in this list.   It was a strange Gothic structure, octagonal in plan, built in 1794, from designs made by James Adam. The main entrance survives with the octagonal clerestory behind, while alongside is the Adam " castle style " manse.

THE ROMAN CATHOLIC CHAPEL, BROUGHTON STREET   *XIII*

This church, now St. Mary's Metropolitan Cathedral, has been altered internally but the street elevation is much as it was when built by James Gillespie Graham in 1813. It was the first essay in Edinburgh of that peculiar type of Gothic facade which acted as a screen to a simple rectangular auditorium whose bulk was hidden by the flanking houses.

ST. JOHN'S EPISCOPAL CHAPEL, PRINCES STREET   *XIV*

St. John's and St. Paul's Chapels were both innovations in that they were built on free standing sites and presented their whole length to the street.   St. John's is an elegant work in a free rendering of English Perpendicular, inspired by St. George's Chapel, Windsor, and was built by William Burn between 1816 and 1818.   The western tower was designed to carry an openwork crown, but this was blown down before the church was opened and not replaced. Inside, very slim columns support charming fan vaulting executed in plaster, and it was remarkable in its day for containing no gallery. The chancel and apse were added in 1881.

ST. PAUL'S EPISCOPAL CHAPEL, YORK PLACE   *XV*

The other notable Gothic achievement of this era was also built between 1816 and 1818 to the designs of Archibald Elliot.   It is not so competent as St. John's, but is in much the same style with a slight flavour in this case of King's College Chapel, Cambridge.   The chancel was added in 1892.

THE SECESSION AND OTHER DISSENTING CHURCHES

This short survey is no place in which to trace the remarkably complicated history of the various secessions from the Established Church during the 18th and early 19th centuries. The list merely contains a note of some of the structures built by these bodies previous to 1830 and which still survive in the city. These chapels are all of the galleried auditorium type, and for financial reasons are normally very simple.

BRISTO CHAPEL (later Pollock Hall, demolished)   *XVI*

Opened in 1804 by the Associate Synod of Burghers.

THE METHODIST CHAPEL, NICOLSON SQUARE   *XVII*

A simple classical building built in 1815 with a pilastered front supported on rusticated arches.

THE INDEPENDENT CHAPEL, BROUGHTON STREET   *XVIII*

Stands on a corner site and has a pleasant front with a Palladian window divided by Ionic shafts. The side elevation conforms with the design of the houses of Albany Street. Built in 1816 to the designs of David Skae, a builder.

DR. JAMIESON'S CHAPEL, NICOLSON STREET (now Nicolson Street Church)   *XIX*

Built by the General Associate Synod in 1819 to the designs of James Gillespie Graham. A Gothic facade masking a church which has been burnt and entirely altered.

DR. JOHN BROWN'S CHAPEL, BROUGHTON PLACE (now Broughton Place Church)   *XX*

A plain building with a good Greek Doric portico, erected by the United Associate Synod in 1821 with Archibald Elliot as architect. A steeple was intended but never built. The interior was recast in 1870.

THE PUBLIC BUILDINGS

The Royal Exchange, High Street (now the City
      Chambers)   1

Founded in 1753 and built to the plans of John Adam
to provide shops, coffee houses, dwellings and a place of
business for merchants. The merchants never made use
of it, and it became the City Chambers in 1811. The
main facade, with a pediment supported by four Corinthian
pilasters, stands well back from the High Street at the end
of an arcaded courtyard. The back, still one of the highest
buildings in Edinburgh, has eleven floors.

St. Cecilia's Hall, Niddry Street   2

Built for the Musical Society of Edinburgh in 1763 by
Robert Mylne on the model of the Opera House at Parma.
The street elevation is not exciting, but the present street
is not on the line of the original wynd and, when first
erected, much of the facade was hidden behind other
buildings. The interior was much altered but the lower
foyer and oval ceiling remained. In 1966 it was rebuilt in
its original form. Nevertheless, the place is of considerable
interest as the musical centre of Edinburgh during the
latter part of the 18th century. It was later acquired by a
Masonic Lodge, and a hall was added by them in 1812.

The Register House   3

Founded in 1774 to contain the national records.
Designed by Robert Adam and supervised by his elder
brother John, the building was not complete when the
former died in 1792, and the rear portion was carried
on till 1822 by Robert Reid, who, as usual, altered Adam's
plans. However, the main front is the least altered of all

Adam's buildings in the city and is one of the finest speci-
mens of his work. The interior has been much renewed,
and the only room in anything like its original state is the
large circular apartment under the dome.

THE OLD OBSERVATORY, CALTON HILL   4

Founded in 1776 to designs of James Craig and Robert
Adam who, on a passing visit, suggested that it should look
like a fortification, hence the money ran out and it was not
finished till 1792 " in a style far inferior " to the original
intention. It now consists of a buttressed round tower
with Gothic windows and some Victorian additions.

THE OLD HIGH SCHOOL, INFIRMARY STREET   5

Commenced in 1777 to take the place of still earlier
buildings. When the school removed to the Calton Hill,
it was sold in 1828 to the Infirmary, which then stood
adjacent, in order to form part of the surgical hospital.
A plain rectangular block designed by Alexander Laing.

THE ASSEMBLY ROOMS, GEORGE STREET   6

Built between 1784 and 1787 to the plans of John
Henderson. The ballroom (92 feet by 42 feet by 40 feet)
on the first floor is a fine apartment. The Tuscan portico,
projecting into George Street on rusticated arches, was
added by William Burn in 1818, and the same architect
designed the Music Hall behind in 1843 for musical festivals.

THE MERCHANTS' HALL, HUNTER SQUARE   7

Designed by John Baxter and built between 1788 and
1790 at the time of the South Bridge " improvements ", of
which scheme it formed part. The facade, with its fluted
Doric pilasters on a rusticated base, shows Adam influence
but is somewhat altered, as the building is now used for
other purposes.

ST. BERNARD'S WELL, STOCKBRIDGE　　　　　　　　　　　8

A charming piece of landscape architecture, built in
1789 by Alexander Nasmyth, and even now in an appro-
priately rustic setting. It is a small circular Roman Doric
temple standing on a fantastically rusticated base, which
contains the pump room of the once fashionable mineral well.

A few hundred yards up the glen is another well. A
very simple little building, dated 1810, and called after
St. George in allusion to the Jubilee of George III.

THE UNIVERSITY　　　　　　　　　　　　　　　　9

The foundation stone of the building which replaced
that of 1583 was laid in November, 1789. Work was
started at the north-west corner and centre of the east
facade. The great Craigleith stone monoliths at the
entrance were set up in 1791 but, three years later, work
was stopped owing to lack of funds, to the death of the
Principal and of the architect, Robert Adam. Not till
1815 was a move made to go on with the half-finished
building and then a competition was instituted. The
conditions enjoined that " regard being always had to the
part already executed, and to the preservation of the
architecture of Mr. Adam as far as practicable." However, it didn't seem very practicable, for they suggested
there should only be one court instead of the two provided by Adam ; hence much of the genius of the design
was lost before the work was even started. The competition was quite a large affair, for drawings were submitted
by William Adam, Richard Crichton, Archibald Elliot,
William Burn, William Playfair, James Milne, John Paterson, Thomas Hamilton and Robert Morrison. Some of the
competitors stood out strongly for Adam's double court,
but in the end W. H. Playfair got the job. His design
envisaged the present single court but, not only that, he
lowered the level of it some nine feet, thus rendering
necessary the numerous tiresome flights of steps all round

it. He did rather better in the library, a noble room nearly two hundred feet long. The work was finished about 1834.

The entrance, which has tremendous scale combined with a grand classic simplicity, is the finest thing in Edinburgh, and it is much to be regretted that Adam could not have finished the work which began so well. The dome over the entrance was added in the 1880's by Sir Rowand Anderson.

THE BANK OF SCOTLAND, THE MOUND   10

Built in 1806 in " Roman Corinthian after Palladio's manner " by Robert Reid and Richard Crichton. Being largely erected on travelled earth, immense underbuilding was required and made it exceedingly expensive. Little of the original conception remains, for it was very extensively altered by David Bryce in 1865-70.

THE NELSON MONUMENT, CALTON HILL   11

Nasmyth produced a design, but it was too expensive and Robert Burn was commissioned for the work whose foundation stone was laid in October, 1807. As with so many Edinburgh monuments it progressed very slowly, Burn died and it was finished in 1816 by Thomas Bonnar. It is a strange, elongated battlemented tower, possibly inspired by a telescope, rising from a five-sided building of one storey in which at one time Nelson dinners were held.

PARLIAMENT SQUARE   12

An extensive Ionic elevation which bounds St. Giles' Church to the south. The work was started in 1807 by Robert Reid, who covered the Parliament House of 1639 in a classic casing and ran a long wing westward to house the Advocates' and Signet Libraries. This was finished in 1810. Later the fire of 1824, which destroyed the buildings to the east, and the necessity for enlarging the Courts of Justice, led to the completion of the scheme in 1834.

The libraries in the west wing were designed by William Stark shortly before his death in 1813. The upper was originally set apart for the Advocates, but both now belong to the Writers to the Signet. They are fine rooms, lined with Corinthian columns, the upper, with a central saucer dome, being 136 feet long. The original heating of the lower library was contrived by James Jardine with a system of hot air which rose through the legs of small cast-iron tables. The tables are still in place. The stair connecting the two libraries is an ingenious design by Playfair, 1819, subsequently altered by Burn in 1834. William Nixon added the Police Chambers on the east, 1845-9.

WATERLOO PLACE AND REGENT BRIDGE   13

The ceremonial approach to Princes Street from the east was begun in 1815. The line of the road was designed by Robert Stevenson and the building by Archibald Elliot.

An Ionic portico flanks either side of the entrance to Princes Street, and pilasters of the same order carry the entablature along the strictly symmetrical buildings which line the road. The block on the south side west of the Regent Bridge was the Stamp Office, while the block east of the bridge was the Post Office, with the Waterloo Tavern and Hotel opposite. The screen walls beyond are adorned with stout Doric columns with niches between them. Behind the wall on the south side is the old Calton bury-ing ground which contains David Hume's circular tomb, designed by Robert Adam in 1777 ; but behind the wall on the north is an ingeniously planned top lit hall, finished in 1819, which was provided for the, now defunct, Incorpo-rations of the Calton.

The Regent Bridge spans the glen in a single arch 50 feet high, and bears on either side an open Ionic screen. In the centre of this rises a Corinthian arch supporting a panel setting forth a record of its erection.

PLATE 9

ST. BERNARD'S WELL   A. NASMYTH, 1789

PLATE 10

THE REGENT BRIDGE   A. ELLIOT, 1815

PLATE 11

THE GOVERNOR'S HOUSE, CALTON JAIL   A. ELLIOT, 1815

PLATE 12

THE NEW OBSERVATORY AND PLAYFAIR'S MONUMENT

W. H. PLAYFAIR, 1818 and 1825–26

THE NATIONAL MONUMENT

C. R. COCKERELL, executed by W. H. PLAYFAIR, 1822

PLATE 14

THE ROYAL HIGH SCHOOL

T. HAMILTON, 1825

PLATE 16

THE FONT AT HOUGH END

THE GOVERNOR'S HOUSE, CALTON
JAIL   14

The foundation stone of the Jail
was laid on the same day in 1815 as
that of the Regent Bridge. The architect was also Archibald Elliot. The
Jail was a very castellated affair and,
as it stood on the edge of a rocky
cliff, was often hailed by travellers
passing on the railway beneath as
Edinburgh Castle. All that remains
of it is the Governor's House, a
quaint building, very be-turreted and
battlemented, standing on a spur of
rock.

THE NEW OBSERVATORY, CALTON
HILL   15

Founded in 1818 and designed by
W. H. Playfair in Roman Doric. On
plan it is cruciform with a portico at
the end of each wing and an astro-
nomical dome in the centre. At one
corner of the massive boundary wall is
a Greek Doric monument in memory
of Professor John Playfair, which
was erected in 1826 to the plans of
his nephew.

THE MELVILLE MONUMENT, ST.
ANDREW SQUARE   16

Erected with subscriptions from
the Navy in memory of Henry
Dundas, first Viscount Melville, who
was Treasurer to the Navy under
Pitt. It was started in 1821 by

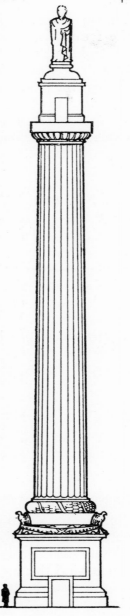

THE MELVILLE MONUMENT

William Burn, with advice from Robert Stevenson about the foundation, because the residents of the square were somewhat alarmed by having anything quite so high near them. It was finished just in time for the King's visit during the autumn of the following year. The statue, modelled by Chantrey and carved by Robert Forrest was set up in 1828. It consists of a Doric column, 136 feet high, modelled on Trajan's column in Rome, but with a fluted shaft instead of a sculptured one.

THE NATIONAL MONUMENT, CALTON HILL 17

A church, whose exterior was to have been an exact copy of the Parthenon in Athens, was to have formed the national memorial of the Napoleonic Wars. W. H. Playfair prepared the plans from C. R. Cockerell's master drawings, and the foundation stone was laid during the King's visit in 1822. Building did not start immediately, but eventually, by about 1830, twelve columns, composed of vast blocks of Craigleith stone, were in place. By then, funds had run out, interest waned, so the scaffolding was removed, leaving the structure in its present state.

THE DEAF AND DUMB INSTITUTION, HENDERSON ROW 18

A plain pedimented building founded in 1823, and erected to the designs of James Gillespie Graham.

EDINBURGH ACADEMY 19

Designed by William Burn and started in 1823, though not completely finished till 1836. It is a long low building with a Greek Doric portico in the centre of the main front, and behind this an oval assembly hall. Till St. Stephen's Church was built, it terminated the vista at the end of Howe Street.

THE ROYAL INSTITUTION, THE MOUND (now the R.S.A.
Gallery) 20

Founded in 1823 by the Board of Trustees for Manufactures to plans by W. H. Playfair to house the Society
of Antiquaries with their museum, The Royal Society and
the Society for the Encouragement of the Fine Arts in
Scotland. Owing to the artificial nature of the site, which
had been formed into the Mound from 1783 onwards,
with earth dug from the foundations of new houses, the
building had to be erected on piles. It was not long finished
before Playfair was called on to enlarge it to nearly twice
its previous size. The extension was made on the south
end, but the north portico was deepened by an additional
row of columns and the side pavilions extended. This
work was started in 1833 and the building was finished in
1835, as it now stands—an essay in Grecian Doric. The
statue of Queen Victoria by Sir John Steel was placed
over the north portico a few years later.

THE ROYAL HIGH SCHOOL, CALTON HILL 21

This fine building was started in 1825 to the designs
of Thomas Hamilton and finished four years later. In
style it is Grecian Doric, but treated with an ease and
imagination new to Modern Athens. The central feature
is a portico which is flanked by low colonnaded wings
stretching to pilastered pavilions. Below, for it stands
on a steep hillside, is an impressive arrangement of retaining
walls and staircases with, at either end, small temple-like
blocks each with a portico facing inwards. The whole
effect gives the main building a very seemly sense of
detachment from the public road.

THE STOCKBRIDGE MARKET 22

Little remains of this scheme designed by Archibald
Scott in 1825, on the plan of the approved markets at
Liverpool, excepting the Grecian Doric entrances.

JOHN WATSON'S HOSPITAL   23

Built on open ground to the west of the city, between 1825 and 1828, it is typical of William Burn's style at that period. A long two-storeyed block with a central Greek Doric portico.

THE BURNS MONUMENT, CALTON HILL   24

A Corinthian temple, circular in plan, built in 1830 by Thomas Hamilton. The roof is pretty well a literal copy of that of the choragic monument of Lysicrates, but a great deal larger.

JOHN WATSON'S HOSPITAL

THE STREETS AND HOUSES

As it is obviously impossible to note all of the streets and still less the houses which arose in the city during the Georgian period, this chapter has been divided into sections, each dealing with an area. These areas are marked by a letter on the key plan and comprise the main planning schemes, together with one or two districts which were not planned as a whole but which nevertheless contain examples of Georgian architecture.

GEORGE SQUARE   *A*

The land upon which the square is built was acquired by James Brown, " wright and architect", and laid out in 1766. The north side, whose centre houses have been destroyed, was started first, the east and west sides followed, while the south was begun in 1779. The houses vary considerably in detail, for there was no design for each side as a whole but, as the maximum height was regulated, they are generally three floors high with attic and basement, and were among the first in the city to be self-contained. In the Old Town, most of the houses were built on the flat principle in great tenements known as " lands".

Charles Street and Crichton Street were part of the same scheme and were designed as access roads. Buccleuch Place, on the south, followed in 1780.

Since 1948 a great part of James Brown's George Square has been demolished in the interests of University expansion. Only the west side is to remain.

Charles Street and Crichton Street were demolished in 1970-1. The future of Buccleuch Place is under review. It was not entirely the work of James Brown : John Simpson and Alexander Deans built part of it in 1786-8 and Charles Black and Walter Paterson a further section in 1791-2. The north side is much later in date : nos. 30-35 were built between 1817 and 1823, and nos. 36, 37 as late as 1872.

THE FIRST NEW TOWN   B

The general plan of the New Town, laid out by James Craig in 1767, has already been indicated. This plan still remains, but the buildings have been removed and altered in many places. Not only that, but the regulations regarding height, building line and street signs have been flagrantly ignored. No feus were to be granted for houses of more than three floors, exclusive of basement and attic, with a wall head of 48 feet from the basement. Now, several buildings are about 100 feet above the pavement. Further, as built, the houses were in line behind the area, but now this area width has often been incorporated and the front walls rise from the pavement, thus making such places as George Street some 20 feet narrower than they should be.

Princes Street has a fine view but hardly a decent building. Even in 1822 it is noted as " perhaps the most tasteless and clumsy line of shops in the island of Great Britain." Possibly it still holds the lead. George Street is going in the same direction, and there are only a few of its original houses remaining, though some were replaced by fine buildings, such as the Royal and the Clydesdale Banks. Of the squares, Charlotte has retained its character, and it is to be hoped will continue to do so under the preservation order issued by the Town Council in 1929. It is unfortunate that, before the order came into force, several of the proprietors had added an extra floor or unsightly dormers. In this respect the north side has fared best, for several of the houses were bought by the late Marquess of Bute, who removed roofline excrescences and replaced such of the windows as had been altered. Further, this side, being the first started, most nearly follows Robert Adam's original plans.

St. Andrew Square retains several of its original houses. Well set back in the centre of the east side is Sir Laurence Dundas's house (now a bank), designed by Sir William Chambers in 1772, and on either side of the opening formed by it are symmetrical buildings. That on the north was built in 1769, and the one on the south in 1781, the Town Council insisting that it should correspond. However, the builder did not adhere to the letter of the law and cheapened it by the omission of the side pilasters. On the north side of the square are a few of the original houses in a simple style.

The main cross streets, particularly at the Princes Street ends, have been largely rebuilt or altered. The most complete portion is North Castle Street, which has been little disturbed by shops. Here some of the houses are designed in pairs with slightly projecting bows, each containing three windows. Some are more elaborate than others, numbers 39-43 having shallow pilasters. Remains of this treatment may also be seen in Hanover Street and Frederick Street, and it is more than likely that some direction emanated from one of the Adam brethren.

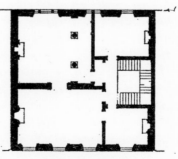

64 QUEEN STREET
first floor

On the whole, Queen Street is the least touched of any in Craig's plan, and in it can be seen very well the effect of the individual houses of various widths, but all conforming to stipulated wallhead and building lines. Robert Adam built No. 8 in 1770 for Lord Chief

Baron Orde and though it is now an office, it still retains many of its delicate plaster ceilings. It is not alone in this, and many of the offices in the street contain charming interior fittings and decorations, often in the Adam manner, but here and there are amusing plaster Gothic conceits.

The corner blocks, which were generally designed as flats, make no effort in the earlier schemes to form an architectural return to the side streets, merely showing a wide, low-pitched gable. Charlotte Square was the first place in which the corner seems to have been regarded as two dimensional, but even here the later interpretation of Adam's design was not so happy as it should have been. This problem was tackled with varying degrees of success in the later schemes.

As far as the two subsidiary streets, Thistle and Rose, are concerned, the latter has, in places, become a narrow canyon, owing to the excessive height of the later buildings, but in the former there still remain some delightful, small houses. Thistle Court, at the east end, is particularly good.

A note on Hill Street and Young Street, comprising the western half of the original Thistle Street (renamed in 1806) may be added. Young Street was feued by John Young in 1779 and built by him. A section on the south side remained unbuilt, however, until 1823 when a Unitarian chapel was built. This was acquired in 1834 by the congregation of St. George's who built St. Luke's Church to designs by William Burn on the adjoining site in 1836. These were demolished in 1970. In 1788 James Hill, a mason financed by Robert Belshes, began developing Hill Street, between Frederick and Castle Streets: completed in 1794, it has remained intact except for nos. 17 and 19 which were excellently rebuilt as subscription baths and drawing academy in 1825-8 to designs by George Angus. It is now Edinburgh Lodge No. 1.

THE EASTERN APPROACHES   *C*

The area immediately east of the First New Town is rather confused by the line of earlier roads to Leith and to Broughton, and the fact that it was developed in small instalments which were to start before the planned area was half-finished. The first scheme to be erected was St. James Square on the high ground behind the Register House. This was commenced in 1775 by James Craig and, as it did not come within the area affected by the regulations regarding the height of houses, he added an extra floor, thus making them four storeys, exclusive of basement and attic.

Soon after this the Trustees of the Register House decided to build on the ground which they owned along the north side of Leith Street, a road which descended steeply from the east side of the Register House to Leith Walk, which had been formed in 1774. The Trustees asked Robert Adam to prepare plans, which he did. They were, however, advised that such grand houses would not sell in that part of the town, so they decided, in 1786, to build rather a faint echo of Adam's motif at the head of the street, next their office, and to let the rest be feued with no restriction except regarding height. John Baxter was called in two years later to adjust some differences.

About this time Queen Street was extended eastward, under the name of York Place, and eventually joined Leith Walk. Sir Henry Raeburn built his studio at No. 32 in 1795, and Alexander Nasmyth erected his house at No. 47. At the Leith Walk end is a short length of street called Picardy Place, after the French weavers' village which stood on the spot. The latter was demolished in 1800 and the land feued to Robert Burn who, a few years later, erected Picardy Place and Forth Street as a speculation.

The grand eastern approach to Princes Street, commenced in 1815 by Robert Stevenson and Archibald Elliot, has already been noted.

The area developed mainly by The Register House Trustees and Walter Ferguson, W.S., has been almost entirely demolished for the St. James Square redevelopment. Only the much altered west side and St. Andrew's R.C. Halls, originally built in 1800 as St. James Place Relief Church, remain. In the same redevelopment the Union Place-Picardy Place triangle of Robert Burn's development on the lands belonging to the Commissioners for the Improvement of Manufactures has also disappeared.

York Place has however remained virtually intact. It was feued by the Heriot Trust from 1793 and was completed by 1804. The south-west corner, however, dates from 1824-5 when it was rebuilt with a bold circled angle to designs by David Paton who later emigrated to Carolina. Elder Street, of which a fragment only remains, was also feued by the Heriot Trust : it was entirely the work of John Reid and John Young from 1799. In the same year, as part of the same general scheme, the magistrates began feuing Duke Street (now part of Dublin Street) and in 1801 Albany Street. These streets became part of the much larger plan for the northern new town in the following year.

THE NORTHERN NEW TOWN   D

A brief outline of the plan of this second New Town has already been indicated. The original layout was designed by Robert Reid and William Sibbald, Superintendent of Works for the City, in 1802, and traditionally the first house was built in that year at 13 Heriot Row, a venture considered to be almost as daft as the erection of the first house in Craig's town, thirty-five years before. Building extended eastward along Abercrombie Place in 1804 and then down the hill northwards, a few houses being occupied in Northumberland Street and Dundas Street by 1810 and 1811. Great King Street was begun about 1817, Royal Circus and Bellevue Crescent about 1823, and Gloucester Place was building in 1825. The scheme, however, was never quite finished, for Fettes Row is still incomplete at its western end.

The earlier streets are very simple but, except in some of the smaller ones, each block was designed as a single unit. The architectural effect has suffered badly in Heriot Row by the addition of upper floors which has thrown the whole scheme off its balance, but Great King Street, Royal Circus, Drummond Place and London Street are still comparatively untouched and form a fine series. The sharp descent of the cross streets has not been sufficiently considered, however, and no solution was attempted other than by sinking one block a bit below the next, with the result that the management of the cornices is not very happy.

Royal Circus and its tall corner blocks with Ionic pilasters were finished in 1823 to Playfair's design.

The architectural history of this large area feued by the Town Council, the Heriot Trust and a syndicate comprising George Winton, James Nisbet, Thomas Morison (all architect-builders), Maxwell Gordon and John Morison (both Writers to the Signet) is much more complex than is generally supposed. Only Heriot Row and Abercromby Place were built exactly as Robert Reid and William Sibbald intended. The syndicate was responsible for the first section of the latter in 1806, while in the following year they began nos. 42-68 Northumberland Street (where only a general control was exercised) to their own designs.

William Sibbald the elder died in 1809. In December of that year Thomas Bonnar succeeded him as Superintendent of Works and gradually took architectural control of the area into his own hands. In 1815 he planned the completion of Albany Street and in 1817 he revised the design of Drummond Place for execution : only no. 1 (1806) at the foot of Dublin Street had then been built. Building began in Great King Street in the same year. In these only minor modifications were made to the Reid scheme, but he produced his own elevations for

Bellevue Crescent and Mansfield Place. These were begun in 1819 and 1820, but the centre section of the former was redesigned by 1824 to take account of the insertion of Thomas Brown's St. Mary's Church. Brown had succeeded Bonnar in 1819, but Bonnar remained a major figure in the history of the area as he held a similar appointment with the Heriot Trust. In that year Brown was responsible for the revision of Reid's scheme for the south side of London Street (the quadrant at nos. 42-54 is, however, by Bonnar, 1823) and the elevations of Fettes Row. In 1822-3 he prepared elevations for Cumberland Street and in 1824 for Royal Crescent. In these the Reid and Sibbald lay-out was followed except at the bottom of Scotland Street. There construction of the railway tunnel brought about the abandonment of the eastern segment of Royal Crescent when the northern segment of Bellevue Crescent and the completion of the western segments of Royal Crescent and Scotland Street were finally put in hand in the 1880's.

At the western end of the scheme the Heriot Trust amended the original lay-out considerably. W. H. Playfair re-planned Royal Circus when entrusted with it in 1820 : later St. Vincent Street was truncated at the northern end and the west end of Fettes Row redesigned to take account of the building of St. Stephen's Church and James Peddie's St. Stephen Street scheme (see H) but unfortunately the linking quadrants were not built. India Street, almost entirely built by William Wallace, and Gloucester Place were begun in 1819 and 1822 respectively under the supervision of Thomas Bonnar. In India Street, as in the other cross-streets only a general control was exercised, but in Gloucester Place (originally King's Place) Bonnar prescribed the elevations, and substituted a single street for Reid and Sibbald's proposed Spring Garden and Spencer Street.

THE WESTERN APPROACH   *E*

Though this scheme failed to be carried to a conclusion by its original promoters, it had the advantage of being at the right end of the town and was completed in the 1870's and 1880's almost exactly as planned, but with considerably more added. The plans were prepared in 1813, and by the next fifteen years, Melville Street, Alva Street and Maitland Street with its crescents were built. Lynedoch Place, overlooking the Water of Leith and the Queensferry approach over the Dean Bridge, dates from 1823. Melville Street received an imposing and rather alien termination in 1879 in the shape of a large First Pointed Episcopal Cathedral, designed by Sir Gilbert Scott, but its three spires at the end of a classic street are surprisingly effective.

The later developments, as designed northwards to Rothesay Terrace, were part of the original conception, but the streets to the west of the Cathedral as far as Magdala Crescent, though not part of the first scheme, are well planned, and the elevations, though poor in detail, are at least decent and orderly.

In 1813 the line of Shandwick Place was agreed to by the City, the Heriot Trust and a feuar named Maitland. In the same year William Walker purchased Easter Coates on behalf of his son Sir Patrick, and Robert Brown prepared an ambitious plan for its development, embracing Coates Crescent, William Street, Walker Street, Manor Place, Melville Street and Melville Place. This was largely complete by the late 1830's except for the splayed frontages of Melville Crescent which were built to a simplified design by John Lessels in 1855-6. Stafford Street, begun in 1819, was developed by Walker in conjunction with James Erskine's small property on which Alva Street was begun to Gillespie Graham's design in 1823. Gillespie Graham, sometime before 1826, had prepared a plan for the development of the whole area, but no other part of it is his in elevation. The Heriot Trust Development at Atholl Crescent, Atholl Place and 3-25 Torphichen Street is by their own architect Thomas Bonnar, while the Morrison estate's developments at 2-24 Torphichen Street, 1-14 West Maitland Street and Morrison Street are by James Haldane, 1825. The northern area of Graham's scheme, designed to incorporate Lynedoch Place, an

*Ann Street-type development by James Milne on land belonging
to Major Weir's Trustees, did not get off the ground in his
lifetime.*

*In 1819 Archibald Elliot planned Rutland Place, Street and
Square, but nothing was done until 1830 when John Tait
revised the scheme for the Learmonths. Rutland Square is still
relatively unspoilt and deserves to be better known, as does
Tait himself, who later designed the excellent Eton, Clarendon
and Oxford Terraces on the Learmonths' Dean estate.*

THE CALTON PLAN   *F*

A competition for a larger scheme than any which had
gone before was advertised in 1812. It not only embraced
the Calton Hill but all the ground on the east side of Leith
Walk between it and Leith Links. Thirty-two sets of plans
were received and exhibited. In March 1813 reports were
requested from eight architects, one of whom was William
Stark. His report was unfinished when he died in October
1813, but nevertheless Baron Clerk and the banker Gilbert
Innes who had been instructed to digest these reports,
found it the most impressive. So the matter remained till
1818, when W. H. Playfair, Stark's pupil, was requested to
get on with the job and to produce something on the lines
Stark had recommended.

The whole thing was far too big and, furthermore, at
the wrong end of the town, hence very little of it got beyond
the paper stage. Even so it produced the largest single
block in the city. Royal Terrace, which was not completed
till well into the reign of Queen Victoria, consists of one
façade not far short of a quarter of a mile in length, divided
into seventeen compartments which feature four Ionic and
three Corinthian Colonnades. Regent Terrace, on the other
side of the hill, is content with Greek Doric porches and a
cast-iron balcony at first floor level. Between them is a
charming little park designed by Sir Joseph Paxton.

The beginnings of the scheme on the lower ground to

the north show considerable promise: Brunswick Street with its projecting Ionic porches, Windsor Street and the columned corner blocks of Leopold Place. Perhaps most interesting are the curious little houses in Blenheim Place, with a portico looking along their roof tops from the higher block at the corner of Leith Walk. Though only a single storey and basement to the street, these houses have vast chimney stacks with rows of pots. The reason for this strange feature is that they are built on the edge of a very steep slope and below them are other houses entered at the back from a street far beneath.

The design dates of the individual streets and terraces of this large development for the Town Council, the Trustees of Heriot's and Trinity Hospitals and Mr. Allan of Hillside should be added to the original account. Leopold Place was designed first, in 1820. Elm Row, Blenheim Place and Royal Terrace followed in 1821 but the last was redesigned in 1824, perhaps as a result of comments by Cockerell. Windsor Street was designed in 1822, Hillside Crescent, Brunton Place and probably Brunswick Street in 1823, Regent Terrace and Montgomery Street in 1825. Only the western segment of Hillside Crescent was completed to Playfair's design: in the 1880s the remainder was redesigned by John Chesser on the model of Brunton Place, where only nos. 4-9 had been built in Playfair's time.

THE MORAY ESTATE   *G*

In 1782 the 9th Earl of Moray was shrewd enough to purchase a house with some parks at the north-west corner of the land set apart for the first New Town, and in 1822 his successor feued the ground for a scheme prepared by James Gillespie Graham. Though Graham was not the same master of elevation and detail in this sort of work as Playfair, the plan is ingenious, and the effect in Moray Place, despite the tiresome changes of level, is dignified. The order used throughout is Tuscan. Pilasters adorn all corner blocks and half columns the central features of Moray Place and Albyn Place. The scale here, as in so much of Georgian Edinburgh, has been much damaged by the removal of the astragals from the windows and the insertion of plate glass. Where the correct window divide has been retained, often in the flats at the corner blocks, the improvement is very noticeable.

Professor Youngson has drawn attention to the fact that William Burn was consulted early in 1822. The executed elevations are, however, characteristic of Gillespie Graham in their Roman detail. Burn's part is unlikely to have gone beyond suggestions on lay-out. Of all Edinburgh's Georgian developments it was the quickest and most completely built, 1824-55.

STOCKBRIDGE   H

Stockbridge was a village on the Water of Leith, and round it one or two of the smaller schemes were built in the last years of the Georgian era. Just north of the river, Sir Henry Raeburn, the portrait painter, feued his ground, and Ann Street was started in 1816. It was extended and virtually completed according to the original plan two years after his death in 1823. It is a most delightful street of small houses each with a front garden, an unusual provision at that period. There is a central pedimented feature consisting of three-storeyed houses flanked by lower houses which projects forwards at the ends of the street. Near it is St. Bernard's Crescent, only one side of which was completed to the original design. Its alarmingly Grecian façade is supposed to have been suggested to Raeburn by his brother painter, Wilkie, but the executed scheme was the work of James Milne and not designed till 1824. In the centre of the crescent, great Doric columns rise through two storeys to support a massive architrave and attic which provide the rooms behind with far more shade than necessary so far north. The scale of the remainder of the terrace

GEORGE SQUARE

J. Brown, 1766

PLATE 18

35 ST. ANDREW SQUARE

R. ADAM(?), 1769

QUEEN STREET (Nos. 64-66)

PLATE 20

CHARLOTTE SQUARE

R. ADAM, 1791

GREAT KING STREET

R. REID, begun 1817

PLATE 22

ROYAL CIRCUS

W. H. PLAYFAIR, 1823

ALBYN PLACE

J. GILLESPIE GRAHAM, 1822

PLATE 24

ST. BERNARD'S CRESCENT

JAMES MILNE, 1824

is quite different, for there, quite small Doric columns support a light cast-iron balcony at first floor level.

North of St. Bernard's Crescent, in Raeburn Place and St. Bernard's Row, are several more Georgian houses ; while westwards is another little row, at Comely Bank, which, though conceived on strictly urban principles, was, when built, entirely in the country.

On the other side of Stockbridge is the unfinished Saxe-Coburg Place, started in 1822 round a garden, with good Ionic pilastered end pavilions. Between it and Royal Circus are several streets containing work of the period.

Documentary evidence of the authorship of the original plans for the Raeburn estate, of which Ann Street (1815-25) and Upper Dean Terrace (1816-17, then Mineral Street) were the only parts built, is lacking. But the close resemblance of Lynedoch Place to Ann Street leaves little doubt that it was James Milne who redesigned the remainder on up-to-date Playfair-inspired lines in 1824.

The hand of James Milne is also to be seen in Saxe-Coburg Place and Saxe-Coburg Street (originally Claremont Street), a small development on property belonging to James Rose. He was responsible for nos. 1-8 and 25-32 in the Place in 1825-30 as well as Claremont Street Chapel (see p. 31). The remainder was designed and built concurrently by Adam Ogilvie Turnbull : by 1834 his affairs were in the hands of creditors, and the north-western side, which had been redesigned as a hemicycle, remained unfinished.

In the early 1820s James Peddie assembled a development site to the north-west of Royal Circus, and on this Robert Brown planned a small extension to Reid and Sibbald's Northern New Town in 1825, comprising the incomplete and much damaged Clarence Street and the severer St. Stephen (originally Brunswick) Street. Stockbridge Market (see p. 43) formed part of the same scheme.

West of the Raeburn estate William Fettes feued a long strip of his Comely Bank property from 1817 onwards. A severe pedimented elevation with rusticated ground floor to designs by Thomas Brown, with front gardens as at Ann Street, was specified. Like St. Bernard's Crescent it remained unbuilt at the ends, the eastern block not being built until late in the century and the western abandoned altogether.

THE NORTHERN SUBURBS   *I*

This large area contains various small streets which, though complete enough in themselves, do not belong to any very wide scheme. Many of them, as Warriston Crescent, Howard Place and Inverleith Row, date from 1829-30. The last named illustrates the beginnings of a new phase, that of the semi-detached villa. The houses here string along a road with the Botanic Garden, opened in 1823, behind them. They are strictly Greek with delightful Doric, Ionic or Corinthian porches and nearly all different variations of the same theme.

Farther east are the unfinished fragments of Hope and Claremont Crescents and finally, on the west side of Leith Walk, Gayfield Square, a much earlier development, for advertisements to feu were issued in 1783. Adjoining it and facing Leith Walk is Gayfield Place, an admirable block of late 18th-century flats.

Development spilled northwards down Leith Walk at the end of the eighteenth century. The best surviving blocks on the east side are 141-171 Leith Street by Robert Burn, and the much spoiled Baxter's Place designed and built by John Baxter both of 1800.

On the west side James Jollie, W.S., began to develop the grounds of Gayfield House, an excellent small Georgian mansion of 1765 which still survives in East London Street. Gayfield Place was built to designs by James Begg in 1791-2. South-west of it Gayfield square was laid out and a series of detached houses built along the south side in 1795-1800. By 1807 Jollie had consulted Hugh and George Cairncross. Flatted blocks of main door and common stair type were constructed to their designs on the west and north sides in 1807-9. In the latter year Jollie laid out Broughton Place, prescribing elevations on the Heriot Row model, probably also to Cairncross's design. The north-west corner originally contained St. James's Episcopal Church ; the corners at Hart Street, which links it to Burn's Forth Street scheme, were not built until 1820-1. Jollie's development was also dovetailed into Burn's at Union Street.

North of Jollie's development Major John Hope laid out Annandale Street, Haddington Place and Hope (now Hopetoun) Crescent to Robert Brown's design in 1825. But like the Calton plan it was at the wrong end of the city and remained fragmentary.

Robert Brown's hand is also to be seen at James Eyre's Canonmills development planned in 1822. It comprised Brandon Street, Huntly Street and Eyre Place, but it too failed to attract sufficient support in the classical era.

In the early 1820's the Heriot Trust began extending the northern New Town northwards and eastwards. In 1824 East Claremont Street was begun to an elaborately detailed design by Bonnar, extending by a bold quadrant into Bellevue Terrace in 1834. Development was slow, however, and was discontinued after 1856, while to the east of it, Claremont Crescent, begun in 1823 to designs by William Burn, likewise remained incomplete. The Trust also hoped to extend north of Fettes Row. In 1825 William Burn prepared plans for the eastern section of Henderson Row but after nos. 2-28 and 32-42 were built on the north side, the development was abandoned.

North of these schemes the Inverleith and Warriston developments were surprisingly successful. Inverleith Row was laid out in 1823 on the successful Minto Street villa pattern by Thomas Brown, but it is not known which, if any, of the houses are his : number 8 appears to be by Playfair. But Inverleith Place of 1826 is certainly by Brown, and some of the motifs used there reappear in the Row. East of it Alexander Henderson of Warriston developed Howard Place to Gillespie

*Graham's design from 1809. Warriston Crescent followed
from 1818 but the architect is not yet known for certain.*

THE SOUTH SIDE   *J*

Suburbs to the south of the Old Town existed before
the Georgian era, straggling along the south-bound roads
at Bristo, Potterrow and the Pleasance. Several houses
erected along these roads, during the early part of the
period, remain, but the first considerable development,
apart from George Square, was subsequent upon the
opening of the South Bridge in 1789. This was quite a
new route which joined up with some building already
begun on Lady Nicolson's land immediately to the south
of the University. Nicolson Street and Nicolson Square
had been started about 1781, and, by an Act of Parliament
in 1794, the line of the former was continued southwards
to make the main approach to the city from that direction.
St. Patrick Square was reached about 1800, Clerk Street
followed a few years later, and so on by Newington Road
to Minto Street which was building by the end of the
period. Near the walls of the Old Town, the development
on either side of this road was naturally rather concentrated
and, unfortunately, neither the houses nor the streets were
very well planned. Many of the tenements became bad
slums and have already been cleared away. Further out,
beyond Cross Causeway and St. Patrick Square, matters
improved somewhat, and Rankeillor Street (1812), Mont-
ague Street, Clerk Street and Newington Road are plain
straightforward examples of street architecture. Beyond
this were some small country houses and an open development of detached or semi-detached villas. Some of the
streets containing the latter were most exclusive. For
instance, Blacket Place, probably designed by Gillespie
Graham in 1825, was enclosed behind gates which were
closed at night, and the lodges with their Gothic gate piers
still remain. Many of the streets in Newington, such as

Salisbury Road, Middleby Street, Duncan Street and Arniston Place, contain houses which date from before 1830. They are too numerous to detail, but several are charming examples of Grecian, and occasionally Gothic, villas of the period.

Little can be added to Ian Lindsay's 1948 account. Robert Adam originally made the plans for South Bridge on the instructions of the Commissioners appointed under the 1785 Act, but it was executed to a much cheaper plan probably designed by Alexander Laing, who was the contractor. He may also have been responsible for the once admirably simple blocks which flank each side of it. The concurrent Hunter Square and Blair Street improvement seems to have been entrusted to Baxter.

In Nicolson Street an architect by the name of William Jamieson was active from 1781 and in the square from 1784. The architects of the numerous small developments in the Newington area have for the most part remained obstinately unknown.

THE WESTERN SUBURBS   *K*

These are of early origin, for houses lined the roads which led from the west to the West Port at the end of the Grassmarket in the 17th century. South of Portsburgh, as the old portion nearest the town wall was called, Lauriston Place, Keir Street and a few other streets were laid out in the early 19th century, and in 1827 Thomas Hamilton designed a new Western approach to the Old Town which bridged the low road to St. Cuthbert's and Queensferry, and cut along the base of the Castle rock to the Castlehill. Westward of this was Port Hopetoun, the termination of the Union Canal, which was opened in 1822 to connect Edinburgh and Glasgow. Westward again is the rather imposing Gardner's Crescent, built in 1827, and interesting for the horizontal divide of its windows, whose astragals correspond with the joints of the stonework.

Only individual dates have come to hand for Lauriston

Place. They range from 1800 to 1824, but most are between 1815 and 1819. Archibald Place was designed by Patrick Wilson, 1824. Keir Street including (the former Graham Street) was mainly the work of George Lorimer, builder, from 1815. Gardner's Crescent, designed by R. & R. Dickson was laid out on William Gardner's lands in 1826. The scheme also included Romilly Place, now 91-115 Morrison Street.

The Improvement Act of 1827 was bound up with the development of the Grindlay family's Orchardfield property at Lothian Road. The surviving blocks at the Morrison Street-Bread Street intersection (1820-1) are William Burn's work, as is the Lothian Road Church of 1830. A plainer artisan development extended along the north side of Bread Street. In 1826 the Grindlays laid out Castle Terrace to designs by Thomas Hamilton and Robert Wright. To this David Bryce contributed the rich mannerist front of St. Mark's Unitarian Church in 1835, but development proceeded slowly, Cambridge Street being put in hand as late as 1863.

These developments, at least in lay-out, preceded the act which provided for the building of George IV Bridge (1829-34), Kings Bridge (1829-32), Victoria Street and Johnston Terrace. The bridges were the work of Thomas Hamilton, but after his resignation in 1834 the architecture was largely in the hands of George Smith. " Old Flemish " was prescribed for the old town area, but not always adhered to. John Henderson's no. 3 George IV Bridge (1836) is the best surviving example, Smith's impressive Melbourne Place (1837) having recently been destroyed. The remainder is well into Victoria's reign.

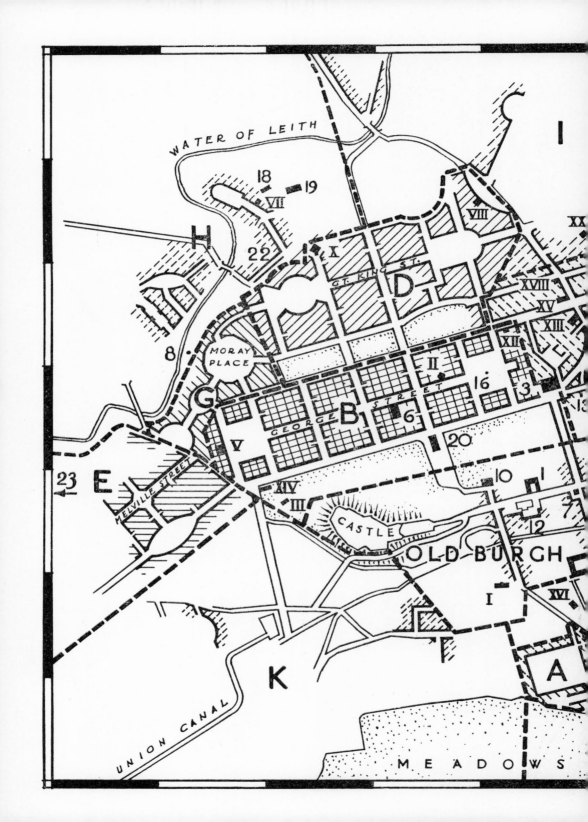